THE MENTAL

Bobbie Hanvey

WONDERLAND PRESS
Belfast

Published in Northern Ireland by Wonderland Press, Belfast.

ISBN 0 9529 439 1 3

Typeset by Priory Press, Holywood.

Printed and bound in Great Britain by Bookmarque Ltd., Croydon,
Surrey.

For Pauline Prior

v

CONTENTS

CONTENTS

ACKNOWLEDGMENTS

I would like to thank Anvil Books Ltd, Dublin, for permission to include an extract from My Fight For Irish Freedom by Dan Breen.

I would like also to thank my good friends for their inspiration and editorial expertise – Pauline Prior, Davina Jones, Sylvia Hermon and Kate Dinsdale. Their help is much appreciated.

Where Are You Going Sir?

A couple of hundred yards down the road in front of me, below the tall trees, the hustling bustle in the moon-lit darkness left me in no doubt that I was about to confront another one.

As my old Ford car stumbled nervously towards it, blackened shapes busied, scurried and stopped. Like a swarm of fireflies, jumpy cigarette tips glowed, glided, swooped and disappeared again in the distance. This was it!

The big roadblock was getting closer and loomed directly across my path. Having braked early to minimise the sound of the grinding of metal on metal, I was now fully prepared to splash out and invest in new pads, while hoping my discs had not suffered too much damage. The grinding always seemed louder at times such as this, causing me to grit whatever few teeth I had and screw my face up. Jesus! How I hated noisy brakes.

Verey-lights lit up the dying summer sky and revealed countless white eyes peering out of greased-up skulls. Warm rain pounded and bounced on the shining barrels of ever-ready guns, and two brown, well-stoned Landrovers, parked deliberately across my path, told me

1

it was time for some more law and order.

An Ulster Defence Regiment soldier's torch peered through a thousand, red raindrops as I pushed the button, causing the glass between us to disappear somewhere down into the middle of the door.

'Some brakes you've got there, sir,' he grinned.

'What brakes?' I answered, letting him know I knew I hadn't got any.

'Now, now sir, there's no need to get touchy. I think it would be a good idea to get them fixed.'

'You're not going to believe this, but on approaching your road-block I said to myself because I hate to hear the grinding it annoys my head that it was time to have them replaced. I'll do it tomorrow.'

'Now you're talking sir. That's the job.'

'You're not going to summons me, then?'

'We've more to do than do people for bad brakes. That's a job for the police. What we're more interested in is helping to keep Ulster free from terrorism, so that decent folk can be left alone.'

His line was straight from an old UDR television recruitment advertisement popular during the 1970s, which showed a very irate man having his car searched at a roadblock. 'Why don't you go and catch some terrorists,' he had said to the soldier 'and lave dacent folk alone.'

I noticed his attitude harden slightly when he reminded me it was 0200 hours, or in layman's lingo as he also put it, two o'clock in the morning.

'Now, sir, would you mind telling me what all this

gear's doing in the back seat of your car?'

'They're my cameras, I'm a photographer.'

'Aye, I see that. You must be expecting World War Three. You've the best of good gear. One, two, three, Hasselblad cameras and a stack of lenses. Must have cost you a fortune,' he mumbled as his flash lamp continued its search.

'Indeed they did and I'm still paying for them. Did you know that NASA uses Hasselblads and there's two lying on the moon?'

'I know that. My best mate has one, but he's only got the standard lens. Best camera in the world.'

'I can second that.'

'Would you mind stepping out of the vehicle and opening your bonnet and boot, sir?'

'OK,' I answered, as he opened the door and gestured for me to get out.

I stepped from the vehicle and the rain and wind whacked me like a punch ball, as the young soldier led me in the direction of the bonnet. Why doesn't the Government supply these soldiers with umbrellas? I asked myself. I'll get soaked. Before I could say, 'Jesus, what a night,' the white narrow beam of his torch was dancing on plug leads, wires, engine and radiator, until he was well satisfied there was nothing illegal lurking there. A slam of the bonnet and it was onto the boot.

The expression, 'Aye, aye and what have we got here then?' always reminded me of the times when I used to watch Dixon of Dock Green on TV every Saturday evening. Only this guy was a million miles removed from old Dixon.

'They're portable flash units,' I explained, hoping he wouldn't lift the blanket behind them and find the six bottles of poteen underneath.

'Portable flash guns,' he repeated. 'What's that red thing and look, this one's blue and that one's orange?'

'They're colour filters. I can change the colour of the forest with them. I can make trees red and the grass orange and people blue.'

'True Blues, I hope,' he laughed. 'I think turning the grass orange is a great idea, but why do you want to turn the trees red?'

'Just for special effects.' By this stage, I was soaked to the skin and dreaded getting back into the car. I had bought brand new seat covers and the amount of water my clothes were carrying would do them no good whatsoever. Clunking the boot closed and, thank God, never noticing the poteen, he asked me to get back into the vehicle and I did. He leaned through the open window and shone the light, which had changed to red again, into my eyes, nose and tonsils.

I hope that red light doesn't make my eyes look blood-shot or he'll do me for drunken driving.

'Now, sir,' he directed, in a manner which he hadn't used before, 'where the fuck are you going to at 0200 hours with a car load of cameras?'

'I'm going to take a photograph,' I said lamely, wishing I were at home fast asleep and warm in bed.

A black soldier, the first black soldier I'd ever seen in the UDR, walked over and then reversed and turned

4

and turned again in the way soldiers do in the daylight, right up to the car.

'Everything all right, Sarge?' he enquired, in a broad Belfast accent. I couldn't believe it.

'Fine, Herbie. Just fine,' answered the Sarge.

'You tell me you're going to take a photograph. Where?' he demanded.

'Tullymore Forest Park.'

'Now, let me get this right. You tell me you're goin' to Tullymore Forest Park, 'where the Mountains of Mourne sweep down to the Sea' at 0200 hours to take a photograph with a car load of cameras?'

'I am indeed.'

With his patience well and truly tested and almost at breaking point, he stuck his head further through the window until our faces were only inches apart.

Almost at the end of his tether, he asked steadily, 'You're going to Tullymore Forest to take a photo of what?'

'Of an owl.'

'What sort of an owl is it?'

'An oul' hoor,' I chuckled.

Tossing his heavy SA80 rifle onto the roof of the car, he fell to his knees roaring with laughter. Suddenly, ten or twelve of his comrades flew out of the hedges and from Landrovers, and an orchestra of ringing, metallic clicks convinced me my number could very well be up. A dozen or more rifles were pointed in my direction from every angle on the road-block, but the laughing continued from the ground below.

'Are you all right, Sarge?' shouted Herbie.

'That – that – that fucker's goin' to take a photograph of an owl,' he quavered.

'What sort of owl is it, Sarge?' snapped Herbie.

'An oul' hoor,' said the Sarge, laughing hysterically.

The entire platoon fell about the place, as two squaddies lifted their leader to his feet and Herbie danced and cheered on the road.

'I knew it,' twigged the Sarge. 'You're Hanvey, aren't you?'

'Bobbie Hanvey.'

'You used to work in the Mental, isn't that right?'

'I did. I left in 1973.'

'You'd have known my father then. Billy Baxter.'

'Charge Nurse Baxter! You're joking. I knew him very well. He was good to me when I was there.'

'Well, he died last week.'

'I'm really very sorry to hear that. He was a great man.'

Charge Nurse Billy Baxter was an Ulster Protestant in every sense of the word - a Sunday churchgoer, who didn't drink, smoke or use bad language. Billy's motto in life was 'Live and let live'. When certain nurses from my own religion constantly lambasted and tried to embarrass me in front of Protestant staff for being in the Civil Rights Movement, Billy treated me as one of his friends. To him, our differences were unimportant. This young soldier was a son of his father's alright.

'I'm sure you miss him a lot.'

'Aye, that I do, but that's life - I often heard him

talking about you when I was small, and the antics you used to get up to in the Downshire. So, away you go young Hanvey and mind yourself when you meet up with the owl.'

'I will. Goodnight and thank you.'

As I drove away from that drab but most friendly of roadblocks, the young soldier's silhouette gradually grew smaller in the wing-mirror until it was no more.

Then my mind began to wander back to that dark, December day in 1966 when I first started working in the Mental.

The First Day

At 6.40 am on the morning of the 4th December 1966, I knocked three times on the thick, grey office door of Senior Nursing Officer, Mick O'Reilly. That door was solid! In fact, it was so solid I wondered how my feeble tapping, loud and energetic as it sounded to me, could ever make its way through and be heard on the other side.

This was not the kind of door you met every day. It was not one you pushed or pulled, as directed by neat little name plates at eye level and forgot about the second it let you through. This was the real thing. It made me realise that for years I had been opening and closing fakes - just hollow, stupid, rectangles of swinging cardboard.

'Good morning, Nurse Hanvey,' he smiled as he finally opened the door at last, 'you're very welcome.'

'Thank you, Mr O'Reilly, and good morning to you too, sir.'

'The first thing we do at Downshire before we begin work, Nurse Hanvey, is to have a good hearty breakfast in the staff canteen. The canteen's this way,' he pointed, as we started walking.

Within minutes, we had sat down to grapefruit,

Cornflakes and the best bacon and egg I had ever tasted. A full pot of tea, complete with cosy, sat on the table between us. This, remember, was in the days before the dusty tea bag became popular.

We walked briskly through what seemed to be endless corridors and the dull echo of our feet thumped in time to my heartbeat. At various points along the way, the ceiling became higher and lower and our voices suddenly amplified and were then normal again.

Mr O'Reilly held two massive keys which could open every door in the hospital. I held mine tightly. I had still to open my first lock.

Today, I would begin work in Male Finneston House Ambulant, which held fifty psycho-geriatric patients suffering from senile dementia and the problems associated with old age. This building was separate from the main hospital. It had been opened in 1955 to relieve the overcrowding taking place at the time. It housed both male and female units and the wards could hold up to a hundred and eighty patients.

We passed the Sugar Bowl, where nurses and patients would socialise and drink tea, although not at such an unearthly hour of the morning as this. Mr O'Reilly informed me that it was built of cedarwood at a cost of eight thousand pounds earlier that same year of 1966. The old Sugar Bowl had opened in 1959, in what was originally a mortuary and later a paint store, and had never met the needs of a rising patient population.

As well polished shoes crunched on crackling ice,

warm breath cut the chilly stillness and our lungs experienced a clinical freshness which wouldn't last for long.

The universal trademark of a mental nurse, the long white coat, felt new and awkward. Stiff with starch, it had a mind all of its own and moved persistently from side to side, in total opposition to my own body movements. My badge read 'B. Hanvey, Student Nurse'. I was so proud of it.

Within minutes, we had passed through the green gate in the ivy covered perimeter wall, crossed the main Ardglass to Downpatrick Road, and were standing on the slippery doorstep of Finneston House. I was terrified, but kept it to myself.

'Nurse Hanvey, when you open the door of a locked ward, you close it firmly behind you and lock it again. Now, Nurse, would you like to open your first door?'

'Yes, I would, Mr O'Reilly.'

My hand was shaking with anticipation as the brand new silver key stubbornly refused to go between my finger and thumb. I tried to concentrate and apply pressure, but it wouldn't work.

It wasn't opening the door that bothered me, but having spent the previous three days in the safe confines of the nurses' home, my brain was saturated to bursting point with stories of madness, post mortems and suicides. These tales had been gleefully recounted by other members of the junior nursing staff - and all for my benefit. Some benefit!

My mind was running so fast I could hear it tick - this

new world that I'd never seen before, was now only inches away. Mr O'Reilly must have encountered people like me who stalled at the first fence.

'Take your time Nurse Hanvey, there's no rush,' he smiled sympathetically. 'Your hands must be frozen on such a cold morning as this.'

'Click'. I'd done it.

We were now in the ward, with the door locked tightly behind us. This was to be my place of work for the next month, and the first thing that struck me was the nose-burning smell of fifty incontinent patients. It was so bad, it almost had me taking a backward step.

Urine soaked sheets, twisted like rope, were tangled around old limbs, both active and still. Farts of differing tones echoed everywhere. Mr O'Reilly shook his head and told me this was 'the dawn chorus'. The floor was flat and long like a football field in winter, with scores of reflective puddles of pungent pish, scattered randomly, but with just enough dry ground left for walking on without getting my shoes wet.

Mr O'Reilly explained that 'smart' patients would get out of their beds in the middle of the night and make their water on the floor. I thought a move such as this was even more than clever.

Voices full of venom and volume as if possessed, unashamedly roared and screamed, whispered, whined, mimicked and moaned. Distorted phrases, 'dirty, rotten bastard', 'your fuckin' arse is stinking', 'your mother's a hoor' and 'shove it up your cunt' reverberated from the bedposts at difficult to determine locations within the ward and quickly shocked me into this new reality.

Mr O'Reilly, who was a genuinely religious man and a daily communicant, looked at me in a sympathetic almost apologetic way, obviously embarrassed by the strong language. I felt it was now my turn to repay an earlier favour and this time came to his rescue.

'It's all right, sir, sure they probably don't even realise what they're saying.'

'Indeed they don't, indeed they don't. Nurse Hanvey, if you manage to come through today you'll make a great nurse.'

I nodded, but in disbelief. I wanted to pull off my white coat, dump it in one of the puddles and head straight back to County Fermanagh. But I knew Fermanagh had nothing to offer me. I had left it. In fact I had left it twice.

I could make phone calls to anywhere in the world from that cold, red box beside the old police barracks in Brookeborough's Main Street, just to hear a different accent. I believed that if I put my mind to it, escape from such a place couldn't be all that difficult.

Still, I would give this nursing game another half an hour and see what happened, although it seemed like I was already admitting defeat. Soon, things were to become much worse. Mr O'Reilly led me in the direction of the bed nearest the door. It was now exactly 7.25 am on 4th December 1966 - time for my baptism by fire.

Stainless steel trolleys, loaded high with fresh sheets,

towels, blankets and disinfectant, edged slowly yet methodically across the ward and transformed the haze of the previous nine hours into instant freshness once again.

Busy bodies were on the march – scores of them – doing what they had done sixty years ago, only doing it all over again. Some were wearing those old Ebeneezer style nightshirts, which ended just below the knee, whilst others were stark naked. They were heading to the 'churches and offices', to the 'farms and factories' and to the 'golf clubs and restaurants'. On their way, they would stop momentarily to gaze at their own reflection in countless windows. Then, as the outside darkness slowly gave way, the winter sun quietly wiped their images from each and every pane. All strands of society were here. There was no class distinction now. Eighty-year-olds with erections and masturbating. Was this hell, or was life really supposed to be like this? At the time, I wasn't so sure. Now I have no doubts whatsoever.

We had arrived at the bed beside the door. Every sheet and blanket was covered in thick, brown shite. These bedclothes, which had been spotlessly clean the night before, now hung sadly over the edge of that bare, spongy mattress and trailed haphazardly along the floor. Straggly, nicotine-coloured map-like shapes embellished the white sheets and when viewed from different angles resembled complicated works of art. The overpowering caustic smell of strong, stale urine hung in the immediate area. It was almost visible, like a sulphur cloud.

My breakfast was still where I put it over an hour ago. How long it would stay there, I simply didn't know. I retched and retched and tried to keep a stiff upper lip.

Mr O'Reilly told me the patient's name. He was Paddy. Paddy's eyes were the maddest I'd ever seen. A fixed, floating stare ended somewhere three feet above me, as his head moved up and down and from side to side, but all the time gazing on the same spot.

Being the new naïve nurse that I was, I raised my eyes to see what he was looking at, and Mr O'Reilly, who was watching me, laughed softly, 'did you see it too, Nurse Hanvey?' I smiled back at him, trying hard not to laugh and replied 'I think I just missed it, sir.' He tightened his lips and nodded, obviously appreciating my answer. For me the ice had now been broken.

Paddy's eyes appeared wide and frightened, as if being constantly driven by millions of demons, and his scarce skin stretched tightly across sharp bones in Belsen-like pose. From head to foot, he was smothered in a brown-caked shell and his mouth, revealing two rows of perfectly healthy teeth, was overflowing with the stuff.

His hands were also full and he was eating it, his facial expression forever changing, from manic laughter to sad bewilderment.

I was getting scared again and wondered what I was doing there. They had never mentioned this in the hospital brochure.

I had been thrown in at the deep end, but within six years I would also become an old hand, observing the new student nurses with their faces full of shock and disbelief and wondering would they 'make it'.

The Interview

Before applying to the Downshire, I had already attended an interview in the Tyrone and Fermanagh Mental Hospital in Omagh, which was only twenty miles from my home in Brookeborough.

I later discovered, when reading a book on interviews, that the one I'd had there had been of the 'panel' type where five or six people constantly threw questions.

'Why are the Americans in Vietnam?' asked one.

'Vietnam is divided into North and South. Which side do the Americans support?' asked another.

'Which side are the Russians on?'

'Where is Cambodia?'

'Who are the Viet Cong?'

At that stage of my life, and in spite of all the bad things the Russians had done on 'my' religion, not to mention the unspeakable horrors they had bestowed on my hero, Cardinal Mindszenty, for some strange reason I was solidly behind the 'comrades' and was as 'red' as they were.

I have tried to remember who it was who brainwashed me into thinking like that, but my mind has always remained a blank.

'Mr Hanvey,' said a snipey nosed old lady, dressed in

Harris tweed and lipstick, 'why do you dislike Americans?'

'Just,' I replied, and left it like that. I wondered if I happened to pass the interview - which was highly unlikely – if they would train me as a psychiatric nurse, or send me on an extended tour of duty with Ulster's B-Special Police in Vietnam.

Vietnam. They were Vietnam on the brain, and that snipey woman asking all the hard questions had more paint on her face than a sign at Duffy's Circus. My father used to tell me there was only one thing in this life worse than an ould doll and that was a painted ould doll. This one had never been born. She had been launched and had the track of the champagne bottle on her face to prove it.

A week later, two letters slapped onto the floor in the hallway of my home. One was from Omagh, informing me that my interview 'for the position of student nurse' had, on this occasion, been unsuccessful. The other one had a Downpatrick postmark and brought the good news of my coming interview at Downshire.

I decided I wasn't going to make the same mistake twice. I took the bus to Enniskillen and bought a book on interviews, which told me everything I thought I needed to know. It told me how to sit, how to maintain eye contact - although I never had a problem with that, how to dress, never to fidget, never to volunteer information and always to give short answers. It also explained the different types of interviews I was likely to encounter - the panel, the one-to-one, and so on, with black drawings of people and tables and an empty chair for me to sit on.

So when the bus finally stopped in Downpatrick's Market Street on a dark, rainy afternoon in 1966, I said to myself, 'this is it!' In reality, it was a dull and unimaginative day, with most of whatever light there was, and there wasn't much, being splashed in my direction from a row of bleak shop windows.

People stood bunched in doorways, hoping for a break in the deluge. They waited with still, expressionless faces, as if expecting a funeral to pass them. Anyone who did brave the elements, did so with their head down, collar up, and with frozen hands buried deep in wet, uncomfortable pockets. Sightseeing was well and truly out of the question.

As I crossed the street to ask for directions to Downshire Hospital, I felt a sharp tug on the back of my overcoat.

'Jesus Christ! You scared the life out of me. What's wrong?' I asked, as I turned and faced him. This guy was a 'stranger spotter' by profession and he was right first time.

'Could you spare a few bob for an ould drink, brother?' he smiled through broken, blackened teeth.

'I'm afraid not, I have no job and no money, I'm in the same boat as yourself.'

'And what boat would that be, brother,' he sneered sarcastically.

'The Titanic.'

'Aw, fuck you, you smart bastard and the donkey you rode in on,' he snapped, as he wheeled round and headed into the rain.

'And fuck you too,' I shouted; 'your mother musta fucked a midget to have ended up with a wee bastard like you.' It was not until some minutes later that I realised he probably could have killed me. During my schooldays I loved to fight and would have faced anyone, big or small, regardless of the consequences. But it had been almost seven years since my knuckles had 'landed' and I felt I had, for a long time now, become too civilised – a dangerous condition to adopt in a mad, bad, old world such as this.

A small lady in her fifties, laden down with two massive bags of groceries came straight towards me. She had probably walked this footpath every day of her life and wasn't moving over for man, woman or beast. This was her turf.

'Excuse me, could you tell me the way to Downshire Hospital, please?'

'Oh, you'd be lookin' for the Mental. Do you see that road?' she pointed, after dropping one of her bags beside a clump of freshly cut Christmas trees.

'I do,' I nodded in total agreement.

'Well, keep following that road for a mile or so and when you get that far you'll be almost there and you could always ask somebody else. I'm glad it's you who's goin' there and not me,' she laughed.

'I don't mind going there, but if they let me out when I arrive, then that's when I'll start worrying,' I smiled.

She immediately stopped laughing, gave me a strange vacant look and waddled off into the rapidly falling darkness, glancing over her shoulder at regular intervals to ensure I was heading in the opposite direction.

I walked through the main gates of Downshire Hospital and followed the road which swept along to the right, climbing slightly up-hill, every step providing me with a wider view of the biggest, most serious building I'd ever seen. Dozens of ancient beech trees helped to reduce the looming menace that overwhelmed me more with every passing second. The windows, and there seemed to be millions of them, hung like lonely picture frames, complete with silent, distant faces.

Seated in the Chief Male Nurse's office I couldn't help but notice the big, matt black telephone, which looked like it weighed a ton. Mr Lees was a tall man and even when seated, he towered over me as I sat on the other side of his dark, shiny desk. His black three-piece suit, with matching tie, neatly knotted between the whitest starched collar imaginable, immediately made me feel shabby, even though I thought I'd dressed up as best I could for an occasion such as this.

'Mr Lees, sir,' I began, 'I left school at fifteen.' Oh God, I'd just volunteered information and the book warned me not to impart any.

'So did I, son, don't worry about it,' he reassured me. 'I hear you play the guitar and sing.'

'Yes, sir, I do indeed. I play on the radio. The BBC.'

'I heard that', he murmured, and then proceeded to tell me that music and song was becoming a very important part of his new programme at Downshire and was most therapeutic for the patients.

'From next week,' he went on, 'the Christmas ward parties will begin and continue right up to the New Year. If you like you can start work in a few days time on December the fourth, and you will be given time off work, in the afternoons and at night to entertain the patients. Would you like the job?'

I was thunderstruck! I didn't know what to expect on the wards or what might await me, but I didn't care. I simply couldn't believe my luck. Imagine reading that book on interviews three times and all for nothing. What a waste of time! Mr Lees, in his soft, rich, Scots burr had just elevated my station in life to that of student nurse, which had been for some time now my main ambition in this world.

I shook his hand and said, 'Thank you very much, Mr Lees. You have made me very happy and I won't let you down.'

'I don't believe you will, Nurse Hanvey, I don't believe you will.'

Jesus, he just called me Nurse Hanvey, and I hadn't even taken the Oath of Allegiance to Her Majesty, Queen Elizabeth yet. But since she was going to pay my bills, I would have no doubts in that direction and I was sure Cardinal Mindszenty would have no objections either.

Before leaving the room, I shook his hand again and

thanked him once more and headed off to celebrate with a cup of tea. As I went along the lofty corridors, I felt so elated I gave the loudest, happiest cheer of my life. Two old patients who were passing by started laughing, and assuming I was one of them they began running and shouting at the top of their voices: 'He's mad! He's mad! He's mad! He's fuckin' mad! They should lock him fuckin' up.'

At the top of the steps outside the pharmacy, I sat down and laughed until my sides were sore. Then I realised I'd better stop it, or someone really would lock me up. In the canteen I fell into line with the rest of the staff queuing for tea. My career in nursing had begun.

Old Clooty

The master left the classroom and was standing out in the corridor deep in conversation with our parish priest Father Cullinan. I could see their heads and long noses bobbing up and down through the four panes of frosted glass stuck in the middle of the wall on my right.

Every time he left the room there was what he called pandemonium. Boys would scurry to the desks of their friends, some lobbed pieces of chalk, someone would steal someone else's ruler or overturn the odd ink-well, voices became sirens, and in no time at all the hive was on the verge of explosion. It seldom reached that stage because the master had the uncanny habit of returning at just the right moment to restore order. Today was no exception.

'Stand,' he ordered.

Everyone slid from their well-worn slippery desks and stood beside them. I always found I could slide better in my corduroys.

'Right! Hands up! Who wants to be an altar boy?'

'Me, sir, me, sir, me, sir, me, sir,' they chorused like a rookery of crows.

'Me, sir,' called Doyle.

'Me too, sir,' added Devlin.

'Me! Me! Me, sir,' begged Kelly, also raising his hand in the air.

'Hanvey?'

'Yes, sir.'

'And why have you not got your hand up?'

'I'm not so religious, sir.'

'Did you hear him boys?'

'Yes, sir.'

'And now, Hanvey, would you mind telling me and the boys why you think you're not so religious?'

'I can't explain it, but I know it, sir.'

'Do you feel like standing where you're standing now boys and still be standing there in three hours time?'

'No, sir,' they echoed.

'Well, until Hanvey tells us why he thinks he's not so religious, we will all stand and that includes me as well. Right Hanvey, your answer please?'

I looked across at McNulty in the next seat to my left.

'I'll kill you, you wee pagan bastard if you don't let us sit down,' he hissed.

'Come on you mountain goat,' I shouted, 'come on and kill me.'

Those of us from the village of Brookeborough, with its three hundred inhabitants, were known in the school as 'townies' and we called the other lads who lived in the mountains a few miles up the road 'bog-men' or 'goats'. The bog-men hated the townies and vice-versa, even though we attended the same church, Saint Mary's, on the hill right opposite our school. After

McNulty had given me his message, he looked up in the direction of the master as if butter wouldn't melt in his mouth. The moment his eyes left me, I closed my fist as tight as I could, constructed the wildest swing I could muster, and let him have it.

'Clunk!'

Caught on the right side of the jaw, his face spun round and he looked at me for a dazed second with the blood pouring from his mouth as he fell. I felt like Rocky Marciano, another good Catholic, who could fight.

'Come – here – Hanvey!' roared the master.

'But, sir, he called me a pagan and cursed at me.'

'Ah Jesus, he's killed me sir, he's cracked my lip,' cried McNulty, with his hand trying to stem the blood and at the same time trying to drum up more sympathy.

'Hanvey, come here.'

As McNulty pulled himself to his feet, I walked slowly to the front of the class and stood there. Barney reached for the long, bendy cane, which he had nicknamed Old Clooty, the devil.

'Maguire, take McNulty out and get him cleaned up.'

'Yes, sir.'

'Now Hanvey, before I introduce you to Old Clooty for the umpteenth time, what have you got to say for yourself?'

As I looked up, he stood with his two thumbs pulling his braces out a foot in front of his striped shirt, with Old Clooty hanging on his left wrist, and I knew I was for it.

'He cursed at me, sir, and called me a pagan, so I hit him.'

I was now thinking of 'home time' when I'd have to fight McNulty again in a clean fight to show the class who was the best man, and I wasn't so sure I'd be able to beat him. Still, he had a habit of looking around when he fought and if I landed a quick one, he'd go down again.

'Pull up your sleeves Hanvey. Right hand or left? Which one do you want first?'

'I don't want any, sir.'

'No cheek! Right or left?'

Without answering, I pushed out my right and waited. As he lifted the cane miles above his head his eyes closed and Old Clooty descended. I pulled my hand back, causing him to stagger and miss, and the tip sparked off the floor as the class chuckled and cheered.

'Quiet!'

Taking my hand, he adjusted it to the required position and delivered a quick sneaky one.

'Whack!'

'Ah Jesus,' I moaned to myself, 'that was the worst one I've ever got.'

The inside of my hand was quivering and the outside was smarting and he hadn't even started yet. My hands would swell up that was for sure and I hated to watch them swelling. Six on each palm had me on the verge of tears, but if I cried they'd call me a sissy so I wouldn't please the gets. On the return to my seat, I managed to put a spring in my step, a swagger on my shoulders and a smile on my face. How it stayed there for so long was a miracle. By the time I turned round and faced the master, my expression was as serious as his was but my hands were raw - they were ringing.

'Look! Look! He's smiling, sir. He was smiling,' volunteered Mahon.

'I wasn't smiling, sir, I was gritting my teeth from all the pain of the slaps.'

'I'll let it go this time, Hanvey! Let us turn the clock back to the reason why we're all still standing here. You told us you weren't very religious, or as you put it, so religious. Now be kind enough to tell us why.'

After the hammering he'd given me, I knew there was little chance of him giving me more of Old Clooty. Nobody had ever got twelve before. Green had got eight but no one had ever got the dozen.

'When my Ma and Da say the rosary every night at half ten and we kneel with our backs to the fire and take turns at giving it out, around the third decade I start laughing, sir.'

'And why do you laugh, Hanvey?'

'I don't know, sir.'

'Do you hear him boys. He laughs and he doesn't know why he's laughing. Do you believe him boys?'

'No, sir,' they crowed.

'I can't hear you.'

'We don't believe him, sir.'

'Are you tired standing, boys?'

'Yes, sir.'

'For the last time, Hanvey, my patience is wearing very thin – why do you laugh?'

'Because it's the same stuff every night, sir, it never changes. I know it off by heart and I still can't understand it.'

'Well boys, what do you think of his answer?'

'Not much,' said O'Donnell.

'It's a disgrace,' coughed McBride, whose father was a leading light in the Legion of Mary and spent every evening praying on his own in the chapel.

'He is a pagan, sir,' laughed McNulty, who was now back at his desk.

'And now, McNulty, perhaps you'll be kind enough to tell us why you think he's a pagan.'

'He laughs at God, sir. Nobody should laugh at God.'

'I agree, sir,' added Farrell.

'No one asked for your opinion Farrell. Don't speak until you're spoken to.'

'McCagney?'

'He has no respect for God, sir, or he wouldn't laugh.'

'Murphy?'

'He's not a pagan, sir.'

'Now we have a debate boys,' smiled the Master and the class was happy again. 'Murphy give us your answer.'

'Well sir, when he says his prayers he laughs at the prayers, he never said he laughs at God – that's why he's not a pagan, sir.'

'Jones?'

'Laughing at prayers is not laughing at God, sir.'

'Correct Jones. Hanvey?'

'Yes, sir.'

'Do you think that if you had new prayers, prayers you never heard before Hanvey, would you take a better interest in them?'

'I'd say I would, sir.'

'Now, we're getting places boys. Murphy, you serve at Mass. Take Hanvey down to the furnace room at dinner time and teach him Latin – he'll make a good altar boy.'

'Yes, sir.'

'Right boys, you may be seated. I will now read to you some Irish history, which is banned in this school by the British Government.'

He went over to the big, brown cupboard, reached away in to the back and took out the book with the old crumpled brown cover. Sitting behind his desk and slowly pulling his chair in after him, he asked, 'What is the book called boys?'

'My Fight for Irish Freedom by Dan Breen, sir.'

'And what chapter are we reading today?'

'Chapter Seven, sir.'

He began and the room hushed. How we loved that story.

'Chapter Seven. "Wanted for Murder". Ned O'Brien, Treacy, Scanlon and I faced for Shanahan's of Glenlara. It was growing dark and we were not certain that we were on the right road. I was parched with thirst from loss of blood. I saw a woman carrying a bucket of water and asked her for a drink. She had no drinking utensil, but I took the bucket from her hand and lifted it to my mouth. When I had slaked my thirst I plunged my head into the ice-cool water and for the moment felt refreshed. It must have taken us hours to get to the house. Boys, why did Dan Breen want a drink?'

'Because he was shot, sir.'

'And who shot him boys?'

'The police shot him, sir.'

'And why did the police shoot Dan, boys?'

'Because he rescued Sean Hogan from the station at Knocklong.'

'And before you go for your dinner – where is Knocklong?'

'County Limerick, sir.'

An Altar Boy

As I latched my coat on a cloakroom peg, the drowsy tang of smouldering anthracite drifted from the furnace across the hall and tickled my nose. I could have stayed there all day. Standing with his back to the burning fire-box, Murphy overturned two empty milk crates and told me to take a seat.

'You'll have to learn all this stuff off by heart,' he said, handing me a slim book full to the brim with strange words printed in red and black.

'Is it hard to learn?'

'It looks harder than it is. You'll have no trouble. Now I'll pretend I'm the priest and you pretend you're the altar boy. Do you see them words there? Dominus vobiscum.'

'Yes, what do they mean?'

'Don't worry about that now, it's simple. Listen, right! When the priest says Dominus vobiscum your reply is Et cum spiritu tuo. Have you got that? Dominus vobiscum, et cum spiritu tuo, so away we go.'

'Dominus vobiscum.'

'Et cum spirit of Hugh-o.'

'No, no!' He shouted. 'For fuck's sake, listen, it's not Hugh-o, it's chew, chew, chew, chew-o, like when you're

31

eating sweets – chew-o. Come on, for Christ's sake, or we'll be here all day, ready – again, Dominus vobiscum.'

'Et cum spiritu tuo.'

'Good, now we'll begin at the beginning – at the exact time when the priest comes out onto the altar and begins to say Mass. I'm the priest, right? I'll stand up like he does and you kneel down. We might as well do this right, we might as well practise properly.'

He stood up on the milk crate.

'But the floor's full of cinders,' I complained.

'Kick a space, that'll make room for your knees,' he said.

'But I'm wearing short trousers.'

'It'll not kill you, g'on, kneel down. Hurry up.'

My heavy hob-nailed boots soon scraped out a patch, which was dirty but smooth and my bare knees bent and met the floor.

'I'm ready, away you go.'

Murphy blessed himself. I could see he was taking his job more than seriously.

'In Nomine Patris, et Fillii, et Spiritus Sancti, and your reply is?'

'Amen.'

'See, it's easy.'

'But what does all this Latin stuff mean?'

'Don't worry about that, just learn it off first. When you're an altar boy, you'll get a book in Latin and English and then you'll know what you're prayin' about. Quick! Dominus vobiscum!'

I already knew the answer: 'Et cum spiritu tuo.'

'There you are now, let's keep going.'

When I eventually discovered that 'Dominus vobiscum' meant 'the Lord be with you' I used to try it out on Baby Armstrong in her sweet shop. Baby was a lovely old Protestant lady and after weighing my sweets and taking my money, there was seldom any change and I used to say 'Dominus vobiscum'. When she'd ask 'what was that about?' I'd reply, 'Oh it's only Latin, I'm going on to be a priest. We're not allowed to say what it means, but your answer should always be 'Et cum spirito tuo' – as in penny-chew, you know Baby, chew-o.'

Within a few weeks, Latin was my second language and the day arrived for my mother to take me on the bus to Enniskillen to buy my new vestments. She kept saying it would make a man of me and it was the first good thing I'd ever done in my life. I was only nine and as proud as punch, 'Oh isn't it grand', the neighbours would say, 'wee Bobbie's doing a great job up on the altar. Sure won't he make a fine priest in no time at all. Sure, wasn't the Pope himself an altar boy when he started out.'

The lady in the 'holy shop' wore big, black sunglasses and had bow-legs. If only her skirt wasn't so long, I would have felt tempted to put my head down and run through them. She walked with a roll like a sailor, as if she was climbing the stairs sideways. She also wore a big brown wig.

'Och, Mrs Hanvey, isn't he a lovely wee man. Won't

he make the prefect wee altar boy? And what will little Robert be needing to go on the altar and assist Father Cullinan, God bless him and be good to him?' She took my cheek between her finger and thumb and wobbled my face. It hurt.

'I looked at Ma and then back at her.'

'A surplice and soutane,' I grinned.

'Well done, little Robert, now let me get your size.'

She pulled a long measuring tape from around her neck and asked me to put my arms up in the air. After finding out the number of inches it took to go around my chest and how many more from my neck to my ankles, her right hand shot into my armpit and she tickled me. 'Tickly, tickly, tickly, wee Robert's full of tickles'.

My right foot shot out and whacked her shin and the minute she bent down to rub it, I pulled off her wig.

Ma bounced over and grabbed me by the hair and shook me and started to box my ears with her big, fat hand. They were ringing and I was screaming and the 'holy lady' was limping and scrambling to put her wig back on.

'You bad wee get,' scolded Mother, 'when I get you home I'll kill you,' and she gave me another shake.

'Och, Mrs Hanvey, leave wee Robert alone, sure he didn't mean any harm, sure you didn't Robert?'

I didn't answer.

Tucking her chin deep down into her chest, she gave me one of those holy sideways smiles and said she'd bring my vestments.

'Here you are Robert. These should fit you to a tee – here, put them on.'

I stood in front of the mirror with my head full of Latin and admired the swanky lacework on the sleeves of my surplice and marvelled at the way my boots poked out from under my soutane. I couldn't believe how well I looked. In spite of all my earlier pain, I was smiling my head off and eager to see how I would look at 'work'. I joined my hands and stared into the mirror.

'Father Cullinan will say Dominus vobiscum and I will answer et cum spiritu tuo – ha, ha hugh-o, ha, ha, ha, ha, ha..'

'Slap!'

Another cuff in the ear.

'That'll teach you to make fun of the holy Latin,' snapped Ma. 'you're for the sally rod the minute I get you home, if I don't murder you first.'

More bells. This time I was listening to the bells of Christmas, all of them. Still, I couldn't wait to get on the altar and serve at Mass.

My first day went well, with Ma and Da, uncles, aunts and cousins swelling the congregation and watching me closely in case I made a mistake.

My neighbour, John Prior, always sat near the front of the chapel and every time I looked down in his direction, he'd make a funny face and stick his tongue out at me in the hope it would make me laugh. Trying to keep a straight face was the hardest part of my job.

Taking up the collection was good fun and this was done with a square box nailed onto a long brush shaft, which was pushed into the seats. By the time I arrived at Prior's seat, the box was full to the brim and he was sitting four or five people in from the end.

Joe Donnegan, three pence. He threw it in quick, hoping I wouldn't notice. He's one miserable bastard, I thought, and gave him a dirty look and rattled the box for more, but he ignored me. Father Cullinan's not going to get the chapel painted with this fucker's help, that's for sure, I seethed. Max Cassidy sat next to him and held his ten-shilling note high before dropping it like a feather onto the top of the money. He smiled at me and I smiled back, letting him know he'd done very well. Pity they weren't all like Max.

The box had reached Prior and was hovering level with his chest. It was getting heavier by the second. He threw in a brand new pound note which he had folded in two and then, quick as a flash, grabbed the shaft and tried to pull it off me. When the tug of war ended and he looked altar-wards, a ton weight of copper and silver banged down on his knee and he shouted, 'aagh!' That was the first and last time anyone grabbed my box.

For two years, I attended weddings, christenings and funerals. I stood in the graveyard in two feet of snow, walked beside the Bishop when he came to the parish, and slogged it out through the heat of lengthy missions. The beautiful scent of Benediction was addictive and it was my favourite. The part of the job I liked the least was doing the Stations of the Cross. I never learned to enjoy the starts and stops around the chapel. Sometimes, ladies would faint at the altar rails after receiving Holy Communion and I'd help to carry them outside for fresh air.

When little butterflies awakened from hibernation during the winter-time and the heating confused them into thinking summer had arrived, I left the boiler room door open after Mass so they could fly in again when the chapel got cold.

Sean Kavanagh, who was Brookeborough's leading mechanic and could fix every make of car invented, asked me to serve Mass at his daughter's wedding. For my efforts, I would be paid ten-shillings and I couldn't wait to get my hands on it.

On the morning of the 'big day', we arrived early and trudged up the narrow, twisty stairs to the room above the vestry, where we changed into our vestments. The room was a wilderness with old brass candlesticks, chipped statues and cracked holy pictures, littering the long, narrow floor way. With the exception of cobwebs and cartons of candles, the only other things that forever caught my eye, were the stacked up boxes of altar wine in the far corner. It was the sort of place that if anyone sent you there to steal something, you'd come back empty handed.

'He'll never miss a bottle,' I said, plucking one from the top box, which was already opened.

'For God's sake don't touch that. We'll be murdered if he finds out,' pleaded Devlin with a look of pure terror on his face.

I spun the tin-top open, took a deep slug and handed it to Doyle.

'It'll break our pledge,' he seethed.

'How can it break our pledge if we haven't taken it?' I argued.

'We're not allowed to drink,' chipped Devlin, 'it's a mortal sin, that stuff's alcoholic. We'll all go to hell.'

'It's not a mortal sin,' I giggled, 'that's about the only stuff in the whole world you can drink and not break your pledge. You could drink it all day and still not commit a sin.'

'Balls!' shouted Devlin, 'you're mad in the fuckin' head.'

Doyle took a gulp from the bottle and passed it to Devlin, who studied it with a mixture of fear and glee. He turned his back on us and swallowed a big mouthful, 'Jesus! It's bitter,' he scowled, wiping his mouth with the back of his hand.

'The laws of the Catholic Church,' slurred Doyle, 'tell us that once you 're an altar boy, then under the pain of mortal sin and the fires of hell, you can't take a drink.'

'But you're after taking one and he took one as well,' I laughed.

'You, you made us do it. We'll tell the priest,' they gabbled.

'I did not make you do it, and don't forget it's my turn to carry the Cross at the Stations on Sunday.'

'I'm fuckin' sure it's not. It's my turn, you carried it two weeks ago,' glared Devlin.

'Oh all right then, you carry it,' I answered.

'I don't care if I carry it or not. It's OK, you can carry

it.'

'I've changed my mind. I don't want to carry it.'

'Are you looking for a fight?' roared Devlin.

'No, I'm not. If it makes you feel any better, I'll carry it.'

'That's it then, you carry it,' he sulked.

I noticed Doyle's eyes becoming glassy. He was getting shifty and restless and pacing up and down in front of me. Devlin wasn't much better. He was on the move as well. My eyes blurred and my two friends took on the shape of ghosts wavering about in slow motion.

'How do you know it's not a mortal sin to take this stuff?' asked Devlin.

'OK,' I answered, 'What does Father Cullinan wear on the lapel of his jacket?'

'A pioneer pin,' mumbled Doyle.

'Aye, that's right,' agreed Devlin.

'You know he's a pioneer and every time he says Mass he drinks the altar wine, so how can he break his pledge and still wear the pin?'

Now they were confused and so was I.

'That's right! He's a drinkin' pioneer,' cheered Devlin.

'No, he's not,' defended Doyle, 'he gets special permission from the Pope to drink. The Pope sent him a certificate.'

'How do you know that?' I asked.

'Me ma told me.'

'She's wrong,' I stressed, 'you break your pledge or you don't. You can't half break it.'

The bottle kept rotating and when I put it to my head

again, it was empty. Things had moved so fast, we'd never noticed.

'You made us drunk, you humpy wee fucker,' screamed Doyle.

'Whack!'

He hit me straight on the nose and the blood splattered out all over the bottle in my hand and I watched it drip, drip, drip onto the grey dusty floor like a leaking pipe – splat, splat, splat! I dropped the bottle and swung my fist in a wide climbing haymaker. He flew back into the cupboard, knocking down the neatly hung row of Father Cullinan's vestments. The green one for St Patrick's Day and the red one for the martyrs lay over him like a coloured shroud. Devlin scurried to give him a hand and thinking it was me, he sprang to his feet like a cat, thumped him on the eye and knocked him through a brace of candlesticks. I knew there was no way of stopping it now.

'What on the earth do you all think you're doing?'

I could barely recognise the black outline and white hair to my left at the top of the stairs, but knew it couldn't be anyone other than Father Cullinan himself, my favourite priest of them all. I wondered how long he'd been standing there.

'What do you think you are doing?' I heard him shout. 'You were drinking the holy altar wine. Look what you've done to my good vestments. There'll be hell to pay for this.'

His dulled form moved towards the press and he lifted the crumpled vestments and lovingly put them back on their hangers. I knew I was for it.

'Hanvey, tell me who started this?' he asked, from a foot in front of me. He was clearer now.

I didn't answer.

The boys were standing to my right with their hands joined and their faces and surplices covered in blood.

'Doyle! Devlin! Come on, who started this?'

They didn't answer either.

'Hanvey, you're sacked and don't come back. So are you, Devlin. Doyle, you can help me at Mass.'

Jesus! I thought, there goes my ten-shilling note. Me ma would kill me and I'd be a disgrace to the parish and the village. I could already hear her shouting: 'How could I ever go out to the Post Office again, you mangy wee get. The Protestants'll have a field day. I'll not be able to show my face on the street ever again. Let me get my hands on you till I kill you...' This would be my cue to run out the back door and hide in Tommy Oven's shed for a few hours till she cooled down. This would take some cooling down.

Pulling off my surplice and soutane, I hung them up and left the changing room for the last time, My days as an altar boy were over. For years afterwards, every time I went to Mass, Father Cullinan would walk down a third of the aisle to where I sat, and whisper, 'come on now Bobbie, it's time to come back – you can be an altar boy again.'

'No Father,' I always replied, 'you sacked me and I'm not going back.'

I never did.

Barney and the Russians

It was 1954, in the days when the Cold War raged between East and West and where walls in most houses had layer upon layer of glossy brown paint at least somewhere on some of them.

My school master was a tall, kind man with a long nose that always dripped and his large white handkerchief, which was in constant use, spent little or no time in his pocket. His heavy brown-rimmed spectacles were mostly used for gazing over, rather than for reading. They had the desired effect of warning us of worse to come and of subduing us in the meantime until 'it' finally arrived. This was usually in the shape of the dull, yellow cane with split tip, which hung on a six-inch nail beside the blackboard. With the accuracy of an army marksman, he knocked flies from the air in mid-flight and the well-seasoned, bendy cane swished its burning message home, time after time. The master's name was Barney McCusker.

During the 1920s, he had been interned on the prison ship, Argenta, as a suspected member of the Irish Republican Army. We were never able to prove this, but the fact that he had 'done some time' for Ireland gave him a certain mystical standing in his own community.

His not too infrequent drinking sprees in Jim O'Donnell's pub were put down to 'the torture he must have endured at the hands of the British'. As far as the Catholic people of the village were concerned, he was one of them and they had long since forgiven him his little weakness.

Every now and then the master would mesmerise us with stories of the 'Russian heathens' who might invade Northern Ireland at any given moment. 'They would only come in winter,' he said, 'because those white faced pagans had never seen a decent summer in their miserable lives. God's sun could never be seen to shine on such people. They are the scum of the earth.'

After a lunch of jam sandwiches and a third of a pint of cold milk, the master asked us to form a line around the room, with our backs to the wall. In much the same way as a general might inspect his troops, he walked up and down in front of us, his left thumb stretching the elastic of his braces out in front of him, until we thought it must surely break. Then, with the cane resting easily on his broad right shoulder, in rifle fashion, he shouted: 'Collins!'

'Yes, sir.'

'Collins, could you imagine the Russian hordes approaching the village of Brookeborough from three directions - from Fivemiletown, from Maguiresbridge and from Lisnaskea - not by tens, not by hundreds, but by the thousands, and not so much as one pair of God's holy rosary beads between them? Can you imagine that, Collins?'

As bewildered as the rest of us, Collins replied in a low, soft voice, 'Yes, sir.'

'I can't hear you, Collins. Did you hear him boys?'

Twenty boys replied with one voice, 'No, sir.'

'Collins?'

Collins took a deep breath and roared in full voice, 'Yes, sir.'

'Now, having successfully imagined that, young Collins, could you once again also imagine why these Godless creatures would want to come to Northern Ireland in the first place?'

'No, sir,' replied Collins.

'Breen, do you think they would be coming here on their holidays?'

'No, I don't sir.'

'Green, do you think they would be coming to do some fishing in the Colebrooke River and maybe when they're at it, call in with Sir Basil Brooke for a cup of tea and biscuits?'

'I don't know, sir.'

'Maguire?' No answer.

'Maguire, are you sleeping on your feet?'

'I don't know, sir.' Everybody laughed – except Maguire.

'Well, boys, I'll tell you why they would want to come into our midst, and most certainly come they will, if they're given half a chance. Ireland is a Catholic country, the greatest Catholic country in the world, and the one thing that these communist heathens hate more than Catholics is God Himself. God, Himself! Did you all hear that boys?'

The whole class replied in unison, 'Yes, sir. God Himself.'

'Back in Russia, priests say Mass on the run.'

Jesus, that's some trick, I thought, saying Mass and running at the same time.

'Bishops, priests and cardinals are locked up in the dungeons of dark, cold prisons and are never let out. Right now, as I speak to you, one of the holiest Catholic men in the world is being tortured and spat upon by these fiends. Boys, I never want you to forget the name of that brave Catholic man, who at this very moment is suffering for his faith and is suffering for you. He comes from the country of Hungary, boys, and his name is one of the greatest names that you'll ever hear in your entire lifetimes - Cardinal Mindszenty.'

'Catholics in Russia who are found with rosary beads, holy statues, prayer books or any religious objects are dragged from their beds in the middle of the night. From the oldest grandmother to the youngest child in the cot, they're lined up outside their homes in the freezing snow and shot like dogs.'

'Now, Collins, tell me this, what would you do if the Russians came to your house in the middle of the night, in the middle of winter and asked you what your religion was?'

'I'd tell them I was a Protestant, sir,' Collins replied confidently.

I didn't know what the right answer was, but I knew this wasn't it. The cane had now taken up a new, more threatening position.

'Hold out your hand, Collins - right or left, the choice is entirely yours.'

He held out his right hand and pulled it back again and then advanced the left. Collins gritted his teeth so hard his eyes automatically closed at the same time, his face livid and grinning the grin of all the pain in the world, and he hadn't even been slapped yet. Two of the best landed in quick succession and the inevitable rubbing of hands took place in the hope that the hurt could be more evenly dispersed to other unaffected regions.

'Collins, Protestants believe in the same God as you and I, so after they had murdered all the Catholics, Collins, what would they then do?'

Collins scratched his chin, his eyes fixed on an invisible point on the ceiling.

'They would then murder all the Protestants, sir.'

'Correct. Now you are beginning to think, Collins.'

Collins smiled one of his big happy smiles and the slaps he had received minutes earlier were long forgotten.

'Flanagan, what would you tell them your religion was?'

'I wouldn't tell them anything, sir, I'd go for the police.'

'Did you hear that clearly, boys? Collins is busy telling them he is a Protestant and now Flanagan, who is surrounded by army lorries and tanks and twenty thousand Russian soldiers, all heavily armed to the teeth, has the gumption to try and make us believe he'd simply walk down the Main Street in Brookeborough to the barracks and get the police. God help Ireland, and protect the lot of us from the likes of people like Flanagan,' he laughed. 'Donnelly, do you believe that an RUC sergeant and five brave young constables, armed with rusty .303 rifles, would stand much of a chance against such a well armed gang of heathens?'

'No chance, sir.'

'As much as I hate to say it and to even have to admit it, Donnelly, you're right - those young officers wouldn't stand a dog's chance. Murphy?'

'I would tell them I was a Catholic, sir, and that I was prepared to die for my Faith and that's what I'd tell them, so I would.'

'Correct, Murphy, well done. You'd tell them you were a Catholic and you wouldn't care if they shot you or not. You would tell them you were prepared to die for your Faith.'

The message was now crystal clear. I suppose that single simple story did more to broaden my mind than any other experience in life. How could we Catholic children, taught so well by old Barney McCusker, grow up to hate Protestants when the uppermost worry in our minds was an imminent Russian invasion. The Protestants, in this part of Fermanagh, at any rate, would have no problems from the class of Saint Mary's, 1950. It was super psychology at its best and I often wondered if the Master was the genius behind such a scheme of outstanding brilliance, or if the CIA and the

Vatican had worked it out between them. Somehow, I tended to believe that Old Barney was the architect.

Years later, when attending the Technical School in Enniskillen, I sent away for The Soviet Weekly. It was a dull, boring newspaper, which informed us of the tonnage of grain produced annually and how the brave Russian troops had spotted the Chinese who were watching their borders. We were afraid of the Russians, the Russians in turn were afraid of the Chinese, and just about everybody in the world was afraid of somebody else. For years afterwards, I believed the Russians to be devious, crafty bastards, for the simple reason that their publication, *The Soviet Weekly*, was printed in London at the most unusual address, Rosary Gardens.

Fisty's Lesson

Fisty always drank at that table. He held court there, gave advice to anyone who asked for it and, much to the annoyance of local people, insisted on keeping the joker in the pack when playing cards. He said the joker could be a two of diamonds, a king, a queen or an ace - it could be anything you wanted it to be. In fact, it could be a great card, if it ever showed up in your 'hand'. All the card men in the village at the time believed it was the devil's card, but if it showed up on occasions to strengthen their game, they were then prepared to overlook such a sinister addition. My father told me that if I ever ventured to play cards and tried to use the joker, the clubfoot of old Satan could well appear below the table. Not being brave enough to test the validity of such warnings, I never used that card. In fact I'm still afraid of it.

The back room of Jim O'Donnell's pub in Brookeborough was Fisty's 'office'. He was extremely handsome, with perfect, pearly teeth and well-trimmed moustache. He had that Errol Flynn swashbuckling look about him which always commanded attention. But the first thing that I always looked out for was the big, rusty hook, which peeped out from the wide, well-worn, oily cuff of his overcoat.

It was said he was a 'woman's man'. He told me he'd been to every country in the world twice, and I believed him. I had no reason to do otherwise. He had hunted the Abominable Snowman in the Himalayas, captured two Russian spies in Moscow for the Americans, courted the Dalai Lama's wife and her sister at the same time and had the phone number for Scotland Yard. This last piece of information was credible, because in those grey days of the late 1950s the best known phone number in the British Isles must have been Whitehall 1212. Every night, just before the news ended, the announcer would ask us to dial that number if we happened to encounter some gangster or criminal who was running from the law. Anyway, none of them ever bothered to turn up in Brookeborough, so I never got the opportunity of ringing the number, but I felt it was useful to have just the same.

At some point in his lifetime, Fisty must have experienced a real frightener with women, because he would scare me to death with hair-raising stories about the fairer sex.

The stories were quite bizarre, and though they became less so as I grew older, to a young gullible country boy of fifteen they were quite believable.

'Always be careful with their privates, Bobbie,' said Fisty; 'Never trust them because in the dense, steaming jungles of the Amazon where I worked, the men fitted their women's privates with teeth! Vicious circles they called them – fannies with teeth.'

'Vicious circles,' I gasped.

'Well, son, it's like this. Here in Northern Ireland it's a well-known fact that most of the adult population who look after their teeth have thirty-two. Ireland has thirty-two counties and the people who live here have thirty-two teeth. It's a plain, simple mathematical fact! But, young Hanvey, in the darkest Amazon, where coffee grows on hedges and where trees are ten times, even twenty times higher than the spire of Brookeborough Chapel, and where those very same trees are so close together the people living there never see the sun - how many teeth do you think those natives have in their heads? Ten, twenty, thirty-two, forty?'

'Thirty-two,' I answered.

'You're almost right,' said Fisty, 'Twenty-eight. They have only twenty-eight. So where did the other four go?'

'I don't know.'

'Well, it's like this, young Hanvey, and when you study it, it's really very simple. As you know, we Ulster folk are known all over the world as being the wisest people on the face of this earth, and being so wise, God bestowed us with wisdom teeth, the exact teeth that prove we have wisdom and are wise. Do you follow me so far?'

'I do.'

'Now, here's where we differ. Most people in the Amazon jungles still do not believe in God. I managed to convert a few when I was out there, but not enough to create any impression. To date, their wisdom of God is zero, and that, my friend, is why the Almighty has not seen fit at this point in time to give them extra teeth. Twenty-eight, that's all they've got, and if they persist in their pagan ways that's all they'll ever fuckin' get!'

I was dumb-founded.

'There's your answer,' said Fisty, as he raised his warm glass and finished the dregs of a pint, which had been lying in the bottom for over half an hour. Standing up, he thumped his hook on the table and bade me good night. His lecture for that day was now over.

For a few years I really believed Fisty's stories, always taking his advice to the letter. But in the end I realised it was just old stories old men dreamt up for young boys and I had fallen for them, hook, line and sinker.

On one occasion and on one occasion only, I went out with a girl who lived on the outskirts of Enniskillen, a town better known to the local people as Skintown. She had easily the best body I'd ever seen - round, yet firm and inviting to the touch. It felt like velvet and it was easy to understand why it was in such constant demand.

She would strip off to her pelt in a field by the roadside and allow the boys to ride her. Oblivious to passing traffic, pedestrians or cows looking over hedges, the act of sex saw her standing upright and gazing towards the horizon like a Red Indian.

During the operation, she would never utter a word or make a sound, and if emotion was a part of Peggy's make up, then she definitely didn't give anything away. It was rumoured, recalled and sworn upon that she would take on up to ten men in succession and throw in a teenage virgin at the end for good luck! A story was told that one such youngster, long tired of waiting for the ten men to finish, kept running up and down the field shouting uncontrollably, 'Where will I put it, where will I put it?' The older men had to lift him on and then lift him off when it was all over.

A week or so after my own encounter with her, I was changing for bed in the light of a bare sixty watt bulb, which came out of the wall at ninety degrees just above the headboard. A light shade at that angle would have looked silly, so it remained as it was, unadorned but practical. When pulling on my pyjamas I thought for a moment that I saw something moving and glistening on my pubic hair, as if some strange swarm was occupying it. That shining, rippling silver will forever remind me of the song made famous by the Clancy Brothers and Tommy Makem, *The Shoals of Herring*.

'What the hell can it be?' I couldn't ask my father and mother because I knew they would kill me. I'd be strangled if I was lucky! On second thoughts, my eyes could have been playing tricks on me, after all, the light in the bedroom was far from good. Even though my fear was growing by the minute, I would look again. I jammed the back of the chair under the door handle and jumped onto the bed, and with my pubic hairs only inches from the sixty-watt, my fears were realised. There were twice as many of them as there were before - they were multiplying.

I immediately thought of her and wondered how she could do this to me. The fact that she 'courted' both Catholics and Protestants was my main consolation, for at the very least it proved it wasn't sectarian. What a relief! These boyos were her property all right and the funniest thing about this whole sad episode was I couldn't give them back.

Going downstairs into the kitchen, which in those days was called a scullery, I filled the big tin basin with boiling water fresh from the kettle, lifted the newest bar of carbolic soap I could find and grabbed one of those big hand-scrubbing brushes shaped like a boat, which my mother used on the front door step every Monday morning. Back in the bedroom, behind a tightly closed door, I told myself that this would shift the bastards. I couldn't see any on my willie but they were having a field day a short distance to the north. Brush and soap were now making serious contact in the water until the bristles became a steaming, bubbling mass of roasting lather. Then my work began - scrub, scrub, scrub!

The war was now on with no hope of a cease-fire. Backwards and forwards and up and down and just in case I missed a few, round and round as well. I scrubbed in places where they hadn't even reached yet, just in case they got any smart ideas about moving there. The Chinese proverb my father had told me came rushing to mind - he that dippeth the wick shall pay for the paraffin. After five minutes of fierce friction of brush on skin, I felt sure they'd had enough. I squatted directly over a basin and splashed myself to remove the excess suds before climbing back up onto the bed once again for another inspection under the sixty watt. They were still moving and I was as raw as a butcher's shop. I'd be eaten alive.

I didn't sleep much that night, rising every hour or so for a body count. I got up at 8.30 am and the first thing I did was check the battlefield. I mightn't have bothered doing so, because they were still there in millions. Pushbike at the ready and my excuse perfectly rehearsed, I set out for the Chemist's in Lisnaskea. Chemists were life-savers in those days concerning anything to do with sexually transmitted diseases. Doctors were too formal and weren't to be trusted and anyway they had a terrible habit of writing everything down.

An old-timer once asked me the difference between sex and riding? 'To have sex' he said ' you need education, but any ould idiot could get a ride.' I never forgot that and believed it made a lot of sense. Condoms, or French Letters as we called them, were well known for putting up a good fight against Syphilis or Gonorrhoea, but the boys who were presently eating me alive and on my bicycle, only laughed their heads off at such protection. They were smart little fuckers all right.

In a back room of the chemist's in Lisnaskea, there I was with my trousers around my ankles and with new shining underpants stretched nervously across spread, shaking knees. I was sixteen years of age. The chemist was a tall, thin man in a white coat and wearing gold rimmed spectacles. Lowering himself on one knee and pulling the glasses down to the end of his nose for greater magnification, he looked closely at the infected area.

'And where did you pick up these boys, young Hanvey?' he asked in one deep breath, as he put his right hand on his knee and stood up straight again.

'Off a – off – I got them off a toilet seat.'

'Aye, that's where they come from all right.'

'Have you got anything for them?'

'I think if you don't feed them soon, you'll be eaten alive.'

'For God's sake hurry, what do they eat?'

'Bacon and eggs, but not many doctors know that,' he smiled.

He calmly pulled out some small steps and slowly climbed until his hand was able to reach the top shelf, which was full with bottles of all colours and boxes of every shape and size. He retrieved a small wax box from behind some bigger ones and slowly descended.

This was the magic stuff all right. I'd heard about it before, 'Blue Ointment'.

'Rub this on every morning and night and make sure you don't miss their heads. That's how they do the damage with their heads,' he said in all seriousness.

'So away you go, young Hanvey, and don't do it again,' he concluded.

'That's it definitely over for me. From now on, there'll be no more strange toilets'.

The 'blue ointment' killed the crabs all right and I was never bothered with them again. It had been a close shave, in more ways than one.

The Railway Station

Enniskillen's old railway station was wrecked - run down and dilapidated. It was in a sorry state of affairs, although I didn't realise it at the time. In 1957, someone decided the trains had no need to run there any more and since then they'd remained silent, enjoying a well-earned rest.

Although derelict, with floors in upstairs rooms full of vandalised holes and dangerous to walk on, the buildings had retained their character and provided Mickey the Dog Flannigan and me with the best hiding places available when we mitched school which was often.

At fourteen, I was attending Enniskillen Tech. In a previous life, this depressing, gloomy place, peppered randomly with black Nissen huts, had been a prison and still had the high imposing wall to prove it. I just couldn't wait for the time when my release would be announced.

In those bleak, grey days of the 1950s, when Christmas cards looked as they were supposed to, sex education hadn't been invented and therefore wasn't included in the curriculum. On the other hand, the College sick room was a constant source of exploration and learning. It occupied little space at the end of the main hall, over to the right and just below the stairs. In such a hotbed of authoritarian morality, I was never able to understand how boys and girls could arrange to be 'unwell' at the same time and end up spending all day under the blankets together. The only stipulation was that if two pupils of the opposite sex were in there at the same time, the Yale lock must not be snibbed. I was sick so often I enjoyed it and dreaded the day when good health would revisit my life again. Sometimes, I even prayed for a relapse.

In the late 1950s, the word sex was not a common one used in County Fermanagh. When a new word was imposed on the local population, people tended to avoid it like the plague and reverted to using older ones their fathers and grandfathers had used. This was one way of trying to stem the tide of progress.

My best friend at the Tech was Mickey the Dog Flannigan and we constantly played truant, spending our days smoking in the countless rooms of that old railway station. Our favourite eating house, the Golden Arrow, was known to have the best fish and chips in the country. Elvis was on the juke-box the day she sauntered in with her bulging schoolbag hanging carelessly from one shoulder.

As I was in the process of devouring a fish supper, she slithered into the seat beside me.

'You're Bobbie Hanvey, aren't you?'

'Yes, I am.'

'I'm Concepta O'Halloran.'

'Hello Concepta.'

I could see from the colour and cut of her school uniform that she attended the local convent.

'Hi Bobbie! Excuse me for sitting down like this, but you may be able to help me.'

'If I can.' I replied, realising that anyone who was looking for my help must be in dire difficulties and close to ending it all.

'You and the Dog spend a lot of time up at the old railway station,' she suggested.

It was in those musty old cubicles of former gleam and steam that the Dog and I cut our eye teeth on some matters which related to the opposite sex.

'And how do you know we've been up there,' I asked nervously.

'Everyone knows that. It's all over the town that you and the Dog almost live up there.'

'And what if we do.' I answered abruptly, thinking she might be spying for the Mother Superior, who in turn would 'sell us out' to our principal, Mr Hanna. I mightn't have worried. She rested her face on her hands in the way most girls did in chip-shops in the late 1950s. I almost choked as her bluntness hit me like a hammer.

'Bobbie, I don't know much about it, but I would be grateful if you would take me up to the station and show me your willie,' which was exactly what she called it.

In those years, girls on the edge of womanhood would go out with boys not to get a ride but simply to see what a willie looked like. When they made the simple transition from ankle to knee length socks, all the boys knew the cat was well and truly out of the bag and the time had come for action. Concepta wore knee length socks and I took this rightly or wrongly as some sort of signal.

I agreed to mitch school the next day and to meet her in the room above the station master's office at 11 am.

I hated maths so much I refused to wear a wristwatch for years. Algebra and all that stuff was double dutch and I could never understand it, so missing a class such as that was not a godsend. It was a necessity.

My maths teacher, Mr Taylor, lived almost beside me in Brookeborough. Before his class each day, he would stick money in my fist, give me a leg up over the high perimeter wall and tell me to bring him back a pound of Roses. They were popular sweets at the time. Some local people believed they could grow on you. He was addicted to Roses.

Every morning at 6 am, in hail, rain or snow, the slap, slap, slap, slap of loose gutties scuffed, squelched and pounded their way past the corner of our house at 5 Main Street. Jogging had yet to be invented in Northern Ireland, but Mr Taylor was already at it. Locals maintained he was definitely the first to do it. No one in the village ever made a point of rising early. Even the cock seldom crowed before seven, which meant few people actually saw him heading out the Lisnaskea Road in his Daz-white vest and matching broad baggy trunks.

Around the twelfth of July, when suspicions of the 'other side' became slightly magnified, individuals from within both traditions would help to heighten tensions by releasing certain rumours which, while harmless enough in themselves, provided hungry minds with much needed food for thought.

Paddy McCluskey sat where he always sat, at the left-hand side of the long, shiny counter in Jim O'Donnell's pub. Always wearing his cap as he faced his pint, Paddy was the best carpenter in Ireland. Being a superb story-teller, local lads who had called in for their evening drink enjoyed 'winding him up', or so they thought.

'Did you hear about the sums master who lives down the Tanyard Lane?'

'I did' nodded Paddy as he took the first gulp from his pint.

'He's supposed to be running out the road every morning before anybody's up,' volunteered Andy.

'He is,' replied Paddy, quietly studying how these young bucks could be taught a lesson.

'They say he does all this running in his vest and underpants wearin' an oul' done pair of gutties.'

'Do they now? Aye, I suppose they do,' replied Paddy, drolly showing the bare minimum of interest.

'We hear you're still teaching your canaries how to whistle Paddy!'

'I am,' he smiled, knowing this line of talk was only a diversion and sooner or later they'd once again return to the sums master.

'I suppose they're good at the whistlin' now,' rasped McNulty.

He slowly and methodically filled his pipe and surveyed them with quiet contempt before quickly looking away again.

'You shudda heard the racket in our house at five o'clock the smornin'. The wife nearly took the hinges off the bedroom door and the 'tares' of her down the stairs and she was out on the Main Street before she realised it wasn't the local flute band practisin' for the twelfth. Oh, my canaries can whistle all right.'

The bar was in uproar, as Paddy gave a fleeting smile and once again returned to his pint. He had won round one.

'You were tellin' us the sums master was out runnin',' stabbed Murphy.

'I was indeed,' he agreed.

'Do you think there's any truth in it?'

'Oh, there's truth in it all right,' sparked Paddy, as he pulled peacefully on his pipe and continued to gaze on his own reflection in the bar mirror.

'You'll not know this, but I'm the only man in the town that's seen him.'

'You're jokin',' they returned, wondering whether to believe him or not. Paddy had the name of being an early riser, so they figured anything was possible.

'At five the smornin' I was takin' the dog out for a walk when your man…'

'The sums master,' they interrupted.

'The very man and him runnin' like a Protestant from

Midnight Mass, with his big togs brattlin' in the wind like a line of washin' and him wearin' the biggest Orange Sash you've ever seen, with snakes and ladders and badges of King William scattered all over it.'

The entire gathering was mesmerised by the pictures he was painting and hanging eagerly on his every word.

'Jazus,' exclaimed one.

'You're fuckin' jokin'?' queried another.

'So you think so?' retaliated Paddy.

'Maybe he's right,' Murphy wavered.

'Well, God's my judge and I swear by all the saints and all that's holy, that I seen him all right,' he said, pulling in very reliable witnesses. No Catholic worth his salt would dare to question such a line-up and any Protestants present did not get involved. The boozers were now busy arguing amongst themselves and the bould Paddy had gained the high moral ground.

'I suppose youse never thought to yourselves why he does all this runnin'. Did youse ever wonder where he goes, because you know as well as I do that he doesn't do it for the good of his health.'

'Where does he go?' they asked.

'Well, I asked myself the same question and that's one of the reasons why I follied him the smornin'.'

'You followed him!' exclaimed Joe in amazement, not for a moment realising that Paddy was in his seventies and slowing up.

'I did. And I'll tell you where he finished up - in the Parochial House with Father Cullinan.'

'You've got to be jokin',' stammered Murphy.

'Only I had the foresight to peep through the window, I might never have found out what they were up to,' he winked.

'Aw, for fuck's sake, would you hurry up and get it over with,' rushed Murphy, who had now well and truly risen to the bait.

'Easy on. Take your time,' steadied Paddy. 'There I was peepin' through the window and there they were sittin' in the parlour. Father Cullinan hadn't shaved for a week and was sittin' in an open-necked shirt and your man Taylor was sittin' upright opposite him, with the sash wrapped round his neck like a life-belt.'

'But what were they doin'?' insisted Murphy.

'What were they doin'? What were they doing? I'll tell you what they were doin'. Playin' poker, that's what they were doin' and enough money sittin' on the table between them to choke an ass!'

'They were like hell,' dismissed Murphy.

'Well, there you have it,' swallowed Paddy as he lowered the remainder of his pint. He knew the law of thirds could judge all aspects of life and this unwritten law had now taken over. One third of the boys would believe him, one third wouldn't and the final third wouldn't care one way or the other. But enough voices would carry the story further afield and sow a little mystery and mystique in the village.

My father knew Jonathan Taylor well and with this in mind I decided not to return to his class when he sent me over the wall that morning. The Dog, who already knew of my plans, was yelping in anticipation and agreed that the Roses would be as good in our bellies as they would in anyone else's.

At 10.30 am Mickey was hiding in the damaged roof-space, already in position to watch the promised performance. I paced up and down, through broken timber and rubble, constantly on the lookout to see if she had arrived. I was as nervous as a young priest waiting to hear his first confession. Every now and again the voice from above would peal out, 'Any sign of her yet?'

'No, not yet. For God's sake shut up or she'll hear you. You'll scare her off.'

Suddenly, a voice from the floor below shouted, 'Bobbie, are you up there?' It was her.

'Yes, Concepta, I'm here. Come on up,' I answered.

I had two major worries. What I was about to do was one worry and my second, and almost as big a worry, was the Dog.

'Mickey, she's here,' I whispered loudly.

'I can hear that. Bet you can't get the knickers off her,' he scoffed.

'Would you shut up, for God's sake? If I do manage to get them to her knees, will you give me a fag?'

'Fair enough,' he replied and he began keeping as quiet as a mouse although giving the odd 'tee hee' to help keep me on edge. Concepta picked her way into the room, brushing the dust from her school uniform blazer. The walls were flaking and she was covered in it. The Dog was silent.

Jesus, I hope Flannigan doesn't start laughing and

wreck the whole meeting, I thought, as I gave a quick glance upwards to check, hoping she wouldn't notice.

'Hi Bobbie,' she said shyly.

'Hello Concepta,' I smiled, just as shyly, only trying hard not to show it.

'Go on, show it to me,' she stumbled.

'Show you what,' I teased.

'Your willie,' she pointed.

'Before I show you mine, Concepta, I think it is only fair that you show me yours.'

'OK Bobbie, but you mustn't put anything near it,' she pleaded, once again pointing at the fork of my trousers. 'Now promise me you'll not do that.'

'Fair enough, but can I touch it with my hands?' I bargained.

'Well, I suppose so, I'm sure that wouldn't do much harm.'

Jesus, I wondered, what were the nuns in the convent filling her head with.

Before I had time to do any more wondering, she had her back to the wall to the left of the broken windowpanes and was pulling down an enormous pair of white bloomers. I was now looking at the blackest, hairiest face I'd ever seen and in all honesty I'd only seen two. As I reached out to touch it with my left hand, although I was right handed, her knickers flashed upwards in front of me with the speed of a faulty window-blind. Swoosh - and that was it - gone. It was gone. Fisty had already warned me at one of his many lectures that black, hairy faces were the most deceptive things on earth. 'They are like watches and clocks' he would elaborate, 'basically they all do the same job, but their faces are different'.

Fisty's a fuckin' genius, I thought.

'Right,' she rushed. 'You've seen mine, now let me see yours.'

In a situation like this when my hand was being forced, Fisty told me to utter the words, 'not so fast'. This, he said, would have the desired effect of stunning her momentarily and giving me more time to think.

'Not so fast,' I argued. 'The deal was, I would definitely show you mine, but you would show me yours first and I could touch it and look at it closely, but you were too quick.'

'I said you could touch it, but I never said you could look at it,' she emphasised.

'To hell with this! The deal's off,' I stressed, as I pulled up my already open zip.

'But Bobbie, I'm desperate nervous,' she sighed, in a genuinely troubled tone. Little did she know that I was twice as nervous, but Fisty had taught me well and told me at times like this to be 'British' and wear a stiff upper lip. Whatever the nuns had taught her wasn't doing either of us any good. I figured she believed she could get pregnant by the dust in the air.

In those days, if a willie wasn't standing, you took it out and if it was standing, you pulled it out. Anyway, I took it out and she immediately asked me if I could make it stand.

'Can I make it stand?' I laughed. 'Easy,' I boasted,

because at fifteen all you had to do was say stand and it did. One word did the trick. Like an obedient police dog. Sit, stand, jump, lie down and heel. It was as easy as that. Nowadays, it would take a book at bedtime or a good technician – but they're usually booked solid and hard to find.

She felt it, rubbed it, tried to bend it and finally pulled it, just to see how it worked.

'Can it fire?' she enquired.

'Can it fire?' I laughed, 'of course it can fire, but not just yet!'

The Dog was still in the roofspace, as quiet as a mouse. I had no worries as far as he was concerned, because we had countless wanking competitions in this very same room. Whoever 'came' first collected two cigarettes. That was the name of the game

'Will it fire soon?' she asked, as she constantly gazed at it and kept on pulling.

'Will it fire soon?' I giggled. 'Of course, it'll fire soon. Just give it time. Don't worry Concepta, it won't be long now!'

Out of the blue, a dull steady thump, thump, thump, thump broke the deadly silence as it reached us from above. It was the Dog and it wasn't hard to figure out what he was at. He was wanking.

'What the hell's that?' she panicked, stopping her rhythm and gazing upwards at a damaged but now moving ceiling.

'It's … it's … it's the … it's the old water pipes. They're knocking up here all the time. For God's sake keep going,' I diverted, as I placed her hand in position once again.

'Will it soon be ready?' she grinned, glancing at me for a second before returning her eyes to willie.

Will it soon be ready? I mused. She must think it is a Christmas cake. 'Yes, Concepta, it'll soon be ready, don't worry!'

'Get it to hurry up,' she urged.

'Look at it now, can you see it,' I prompted.

'I can indeed, I can indeed,' she enthused, keeping the pressure to a maximum. Isn't it grand,' she laboured in a soft Galway brogue, despite having been born and bred in Enniskillen. It was now spitting at her and painting the walls and I was roaring and shouting very much louder than was necessary, just to give her some encouragement for doing such a great job.

'Could you get it to do that again? Could you make it stand again?' she pleaded.

'It takes a wee while, Concepta. Give it time. Give him a rest for a few minutes and then we'll see what happens, but first, you have to keep your half of the bargain and show me yours.'

'Only if you kneel down and don't stand up,' she insisted.

Five minutes later, when I was down staring it straight in the face, an unmerciful 'aaah' reverberated from the roofspace. The Dog had hit the jackpot. She looked up in horror, then at me and then up again, as he crashed through the thin ceiling and landed beside us in a cloud of white dust, plaster and rubble. He bounced to his feet and turned his back on her, pulled up his underpants and trousers at the same time and without waiting to fasten his belt, ran from the room holding them up in both hands.

Concepta stood there in shock, with her knickers at her knees. She slowly bent over and pulled them up. As she brushed the dust from her jacket she gave me a dirty look and pushed twenty Players Gold Leaf into my hand and departed never speaking as much as one word.

Ten minutes later, as I was sitting with dust to the neck enjoying my cigarette, the Dog walked in, grinning his head off from ear to ear, and sat down beside me as if nothing had happened.

'Hanvey, give me a fag.'

'Here you culchie. Light your own, but don't forget you owe me three. I came first!'

The Digs in Birmingham

Living in Brookeborough was easy. A lot of the local men, mostly Catholic, emigrated to England at least some time in their lives and came home usually once a year. Once such man was Paddy Campbell, husband of Nellie and father to John, Raymond and Patsy.

Paddy drove a steamroller and helped build many of the roads in and around the Midlands. His stories of gangs of men at tarboilers and roads, the like of which were never seen in Ireland, held me in awe and displayed an exciting way of life far removed from the one I'd grown up with in County Fermanagh. It was a common occurrence for partners to be physically separated and to travel out of the country in search of work and it was looked upon as part of the normality of the time. Every Friday morning, regular as clockwork, Nellie would visit the village post office and collect the week's wages.

About this time, around 1962, something very exciting happened in Ireland. A folk group comprising three brothers from Tipperary and a lanky banjo player from Keady in County Armagh took America by storm. Very soon, guitar shops throughout the country were doing a roaring trade and the songs of the Clancy Brothers and Tommy Makem were being sung the length and breadth of the land. I bought my first guitar in 1962 and after a few favourable 'write-ups' in the local press, I was getting bookings at parochial concerts and in Portadown folk club, one of the best run musical evenings to be found anywhere in Ireland. After playing there you could play anywhere.

On one of these trips to Portadown, I met another singer from County Tyrone, Eddie Fee, and we convinced each other that there was money to be made in England and in no time at all we were on the Heysham boat to Birmingham. Two boats made the nightly voyage 'across the water' - the *Duke of Argyll* and the one that I chose because I felt it had a safer name - *the Duke of Lancaster.*

The excitement of landing in England guaranteed that no sleep whatsoever was had on that noisy, oily old ship. We sang our folksongs and played our guitars to anyone who wanted to listen and I wondered if the closed down bar had been open, would I have celebrated by having my first drink. Still, the money in my pocket was for 'digs' and I wondered if my father had to tighten his belt in order to release me into the smoky chimneys of the West Midlands. He had never wanted me to leave home and spent nights explaining the pitfalls I might encounter. I did my best to reassure him that the life of a folksinger was one of the best jobs available anywhere in the Sixties, but he merely shook his head and let me go. I had never seen tears in his eyes before, so we shook hands, got the farewells over with quickly and Eddie and I stepped onto the battered Ulsterbus and headed for Belfast docks. Sitting in the back seat, I looked out into the darkness. I saw the 'old man' standing there underneath the street light, where he waved for a few seconds, put his hands in his pockets, turned slowly and walked away.It was like watching my own funeral.

As the early morning train rattled and shuffled its way towards Birmingham, we saw the lights come on in thousands of homes built to the left and right of the railway track. Those little windows high up on the backs of houses had to be bathrooms. A million people shaving at the same time was a business I found hard to imagine, but I imagined it all the same. The vicious brushing of teeth, the pulling of chains, all that cranking and flushing of debris deep into the earth – mile upon mile of hair, tons of human waste, the constant spitting and raucous clearing of throats, kick starting hard-pressed lungs into meeting the day. Here we were, Eddie and I, flying past in the 'orient express' and marvelling at the wonder of it all.

It was difficult to believe we were finally in England where we'd heard but refused to believe that the grass was actually greener than it was in Ireland. It was still dark outside but I'd soon be able to see for myself and put another myth to rest. Grass or no grass, this was the place to be and we soon found ourselves chatting to a man and his wife who said they came from Haiti, but had lived in England for many years.

Pulling our guitars from the luggage rack, we tuned up and asked if they'd like to join us in a song.

'Are you ready Eddie?'

'We left our home in Belfast not so many years ago
And sailed away to England, where all the Irish go,
To the capital of Warwickshire, that's where we made our plan
To sleep with fifty Paddies in the digs in Birmingham.
So roll over Paddy, shove in a wee bit Joe
Lift your elbows Johnny, don't dislocate my toe.
Let go the blanket Michael, don't strip my perished gam,
That's what you hear in England in the digs in Birmingham.'

Either our new friends didn't understand our accents or they weren't familiar with the tune. They sat in long-faced doleful silence, but at least they had the good manners to smile and clap when we finished.

'Very nice, very nice,' they applauded, probably thinking that these Irish nutcases might rob and murder them at any given moment.

We turned right, out of New Street station and walked and talked and begged directions to Bristol Road.

'Go through the Bullring man,' they said in accents we found slightly strange but pleasant and friendly. We thought they were taking a hand out of us. Imagine a bullring in the middle of Birmingham! Eventually, we had to admit they were right and soon the chapel we'd been looking for came into view. It was named after an Italian saint who had done great work nursing the dying and patients suffering from leprosy - the Church of St Catherine of Sienna. It was a sight for sore eyes and made me proud to be a Catholic.

At the door where the congregation spilled out onto the street, we were told that Father Bryans was saying Mass and would see us later. A kindly man, sporting the legendary 'pioneer pin', with grey, neatly groomed hair and Irish black eyebrows, ushered us down a flight of steps directly underneath the thousand or so worshippers.

The basement was the biggest bar and club I'd ever seen, with hundreds of beer glasses at various stages of completion, littering tables as far as the eye could see, stale and musty, obvious remnants of the night before.

'Make yourselves at home lads and grab a sleep. You must be exhausted after your long journey. Father Bryans will see you later.'

Clearing two tables of their previous night's cargo, we used our rucksacks as pillows and fell fast asleep. Some time later, probably the length of a Mass or two, we were abruptly wakened by one of the oldest instruments of Irish tradition – a squealing microphone. Before concerts began in every parochial hall in Ireland – and Birmingham seemed little different – someone would walk up to the mike and say, 'testing, one, two, three, testing, one, two, three, four' and then tap it with his finger, or his knuckle if an old hand, making it squeal. My father always maintained that the Irish loved tampering with microphones.

Lying on my back on the beer table and looking

straight up into the air, what did I see? Only the biggest black man I'd ever seen, armed with a Spanish guitar and singing *'Shall my soul pass through old Ireland'*. I couldn't believe my ears. I glanced over at Eddie and there he was – eyes and mouth wide open in shock and amazement, taking in what I'd just seen. He looked at me and I looked at him and he looked at me again.

Then, a hand from behind touched my shoulder.

'Jesus Christ!' I jumped.

'No, unfortunately not boys, Father Bryans, and I'm very pleased to meet you. Right! Gather up your gear and follow me. Everything's arranged.'

His approach was completely business like and impersonal and not having encountered this attitude before I felt somewhat disappointed. My mother's last words of caustic warning sprang back to mind: 'If you think Brookeborough's bad, wait until you see Birmingham'. Back home, even when squaring up to a fight with a friend, we always spoke and shouted at each other for at least twenty minutes before saying, 'Aw, fuck this' and landing the first blow. Mother was right. Things were different here. As his dusty Ford Cortina ate up roads and streets and more roads and streets, I found myself getting buried deeper and deeper in Birmingham and wondered if I wanted out of the place to go home, how I would manage it.

'You're now in Balsall Heath, boys. Speedwell Road, where your new home is, is straight in front of you. Don't forget to keep your mouths shut, your ears open and yourselves to yourselves and you'll be grand. If you have any problems, you'll get me at the Parochial House. Here's my number.'

When we pulled up outside the digs, it was one-thirty in the afternoon. Father Bryans did a hurried introduction to our landlady, Nora Connolly, who was originally from the County Clare. She showed us to our room and told us the rules of the house, which included 'no women and no fightin'. After that, she got her one week's rent in advance and led us to the dinner table.

A Quiet Walk

It was home from home all right - well almost. The Irish stew, which resembled soup, had apparently been put through a strainer. Searching for any accidental chunks of meat I soon discovered, was a useless pastime.

'Hiya boys, I'm George Bell from Portadown. You don't need a bell on yer bike when yer knickers are ringin', ha, ha, ha, ha, ha and double ha. These pair of miseries are Dermot and Brian from Kerry in the Free State and if they're ever lost, you'll find them over in the chapel. I couldn't help but notice you proddin' the bowl for beef. Well, the only place in England you'll get beef is in a butcher's shop. Do you pair o' boys fancy a quiet walk and I'll show you some of the local beauty spots? It'll help drum up an appetite for tomorrow's dinner and, in case you're interested, it's more Irish stew.'

'A good idea,' said Eddie. 'Come on Hanvey, let's go.'

In the wide expanse of green parklands opposite, children played ball and sang nursery rhymes and a maze of revolving skipping ropes sliced under nimble feet that appeared never to touch the ground.

'It's a black area,' announced Eddie.

I'd never seen a black person in Brookeborough in my life.

'Aye, look that's the mosque,' pointed George, 'wait till you see what they get up to at weekends. There's more fights in there than there is at Madison Square Gardens. The ambulances never stop. They just can't agree among themselves. Locals call it the 'bucket of blood'. They're fightin' at five in the mornin', skinning each other alive. The cops never leave the place.'

Jesus, what a name for a church, I thought. 'Would they hit us, you know us Irish, strangers in the place?'

'No way, not a chance,' boasted George. They're lovely people, they're like us – it's themselves they don't like. You know, like us at home.'

'Aye, I see what you mean,' nodded Eddie in agreement.

'What does that street sign say, young Hanvey.'

'Varna Road.'

'Cor-rect! You have just stepped into the most famous street, not only in Birmingham, but in the whole of England and that includes the British Isles as well.'

'What do they make up here?' I asked.

'What do they make? I'll tell you what they make. They make two things, but I'm not tellin' you yet. It's not pottery.'

'They make nothing. Fuck this, I'm wrecked. I think I'll go back to bed,' I replied in total disgust at being taken on a wild goose chase.

'There youse are now, boys,' chirped George, 'you wouldn't see a sight like that where the mountains of

Mourne sweep down to the sea.'

'Jesus Christ,' gulped Eddie, a good Catholic and as religious as sin, 'this must be one of the friendliest countries in the world. Is it any wonder the half of Fermanagh lives in Birmingham.'

'Look! Look! They're wagging us in,' I pointed and observed the expressions of delight on my friend's faces.

'Would you look at the legs on the one on the right,' leered George, 'as fine a mare as ever dropped a foal. She'll do me if there's no advance on three pounds ten. Now, I'll tell you pair o'boys what they make up here – love and money – that's what they make. It's the oldest industry in England and it's alive and well in every house in this block.'

This was definitely more rewarding than a Sunday afternoon in Bundoran or a fortnight's holiday in Portrush.

As we stood, with hands in pockets gazing over the chest high hedge even though there was equally good vision from the gate and pathway to our right, a big bay window held us enthralled, hypnotised and spellbound. Only fifteen or twenty yards away, those three healthy looking girls seated at the table began moving their legs, licking their fingers and squirming on their chairs like a bucket of reptiles.

'How much money have youse on ye?' asked George, who had begun smiling and clapping his hands together as if he had just sold a horse. He was ecstatic.

'Well, I've only got enough for my digs.'

'Same here,' lamented Eddie, 'and don't forget we've

no work yet. Sure we don't even know where the folkclubs are. No, I couldn't afford to go into a place like that.'

'How much do they charge,' I asked.

'A fiver,' replied George, an obvious veteran of Birmingham's back streets.

'A fiver! Jesus! Do we get bed and breakfast as well,' grunted Eddie in amazement at the high cost of living in Balsall Heath.

'All you get is what you want,' rhymed George, 'thirty minutes is all you get and the clock starts ticking the minute you put one foot over the doorstep. It takes you to be ready the minute you g'win. One minute over the half-hour on her stop watch and it's another fiver. They work by time and motion.'

'But,' enquired Eddie, wanting to get down to basic economics, 'what happens if it only takes you ten minutes?'

'It's still a fiver but she'll let you chat her for the rest of the time and you'll be glad of that 'cos nobody ever talks to you over here.'

The girls in the window were now fighting for attention, showing us the tops of their black nylons and the death-like white skin just above, which was shouting 'come on boys'.

The dark one, whom I had already christened Black Maria, was busy applying the fire-brigade red lipstick and she began licking her lips like a cat and smiling her head off. I wasn't sure if she was laughing at us or simply carrying on.

'Fuck!' gasped Eddie in deep shock; 'did you see that?'

'See what?' I asked.

'What was it?' sparked George.

'When you pair of pricks were arguing the toss, the big blonde one pulled up her jumper and flashed her diddies at me. She shook them up and down. Christ! You shoulda seen it!'

'Aye,' said George in disbelief, 'I supposed she used a flash lamp?'

'Were they big?' I probed, hoping he was telling the truth and she'd do it again.

'Big!' Eddie panted, looking as if he was about to take a heart attack, 'Big! Jesus! They're the biggest I've ever seen and I've seen plenty in mid-Ulster. She could suckle a young calf on them pair o'boys.'

'Aye,' said George. 'I suppose you're telling us she had enough there for the three of us.'

'And half the population of Portadown, including the entire Orange Order,' he added, almost puce in the face from the experience.

'Go on girl, do it again,' I cheered.

'Yahoo,' roared George in solidarity, 'come on ye girl ye'.

A few of the ordinary decent folk on the other side of the street behind us, pulled down their sash windows and shouted stuff like, 'shutthefuckuppaddy.'

If Eddie hated one thing in life, that one thing was being called a Paddy.

'Up the IRA, you limey fuckers,' he roared, 'come on down and I'll give you a taste of my shilleleah, you yella bastards.'

'For Christ's sake, Eddie, shut up. They could gang up and kill us.'

'Fuck the IRA,' shouted George, 'why don't you keep them bastards out of it. To hell with the Republic and God Save the Queen.'

Northern Ireland was now in Birmingham and a few Englishmen up in the windows had us at each other's throats.

By now, the girls were in hysterics and almost falling off their chairs. Then suddenly, they stood up and strode towards us in military formation and stopped at the window. We looked at each other and then at them and all thoughts of politics were gone just as speedily as they'd arrived. They stood at ease with active fingers busily undoing blouse buttons and very soon six of the biggest, healthiest looking diddies in Balsall Heath were being joggled up and down with the palms of well experienced hands. This was the very thing the priest at home had warned us about. This was the top of the scale in temptation.

'Come on back to the digs,' I said. 'We have no money and I've never been out with women like that before. If the girls in Northern Ireland carried on like that, the Royal Ulster Constabulary would intern them without trial.'

'Our police force,' injected George.

'Aye,' clipped Eddie, 'they'd probably ride them first, the black bastards. I think you're right. I have no money either and I can't take any more of this window-shopping. We'll go back to the digs and get some shut eye.'

As we approached the corner of Speedwell Road, George from Portadown was still standing on the footpath looking over the hedge whistling the Sash and gazing at the bay window, occasionally glancing after us to see if we were still watching him.

Up in our bedroom, we gleefully recounted our newest and biggest experience, jumped into bed and fell fast asleep. All at once I was back in Brookeborough on one of those balmy summer days. As we walked down the Well Road with the tar bubbling and sticking to our shoes, I smiled at Maria and she winked at me. This was romance at its best. Neighbours out walking their dogs, would occasionally pull one from the burning tar and carry it, only to ruin a good suit or frock with black paw marks that would never be removed on a washboard.

'Are you not going to introduce us to your new girlfriend?' they asked, with much emphasis being put on the 'new'.

'Your father mentioned you'd be taking her 'over'. She's from Birmingham isn't she?'

'Here's John Murphy, Maria. He's a terrific tenor and the best wit in the village.'

'Well, Bob,' smiled John, 'you have a better eye in your head than she has.'

On the verdant banks of the Colebrook River, the wasps were wending their way through the rushes, trying to seek out soft targets.

'Well, Maria, isn't Northern Ireland great? The people are the friendliest in the world. They even kill you with a smile.'

'It sure is a beautiful place,' she replied, 'a million miles from the hustle and bustle of Birmingham.'

Because of her performance in the window, I assumed she probably wasn't a regular churchgoer, but then when you consider the antics of Mary Magdalen it was quite possible I was lying beside a potential saint.

The Fermanagh sun was belting down, as we lay on the riverbank and listened to the birds chirping, the salmon leaping, the cows mooing and the lazy bees buzzing.

'Jesus. God is good to the Protestants,' I said. 'Here we are on the twelfth of July and the sun is splitting the rocks. Old Minnie Heaney, an ex-IRA woman from the 1920s who lived beside us, used to say, 'I hope the twelfth is so hot this year, they all get sun-stroke and they have to shovel them into the ambulances.'

'But I'm Church of England,' whimpered Maria, as she rolled over in anger, turning her back on me. In order to deliver some comfort, my hands immediately cupped her two big Balsall beauties. I felt something in my trousers stir and take on a life of its own, as I moved closer and pushed myself up against her. I felt a jolt as her right leg drew back and nearly broke my shinbone.

My eyes opened abruptly as Eddie's fist came straight at me, but I was too slow.

'Whack!'

All of a sudden, six army blankets shot over the end of the bed, as he jumped over me and landed with a thump on the oilcloth, sliding on the small mat as he tried to steady himself and crashing backwards into the wardrobe when he couldn't.

'Is everything all right up there,' called Mrs Connolly from the bottom of the stairs.

'Ye, ye, yes – everything's fine,' stuttered Eddie, as he jumped to his feet and commenced pulling on his trousers.

'Now, you listen to me Hanvey, you fuckin' fruit, if you ever do that again I'm leaving … but before I go I'll kill you first.'

I broke into uncontrollable, hysterical laughter at the idea of being called a fruit and this made him twice as mad. He was standing there, pale, frightened and livid, with a fierce grip on his trousers.

'If it's one thing I hate, it's fuckin' fruits and go on – just, just go on and try a stunt like that again, till - till you see what happens … you … you fuckin' fruity bastard.'

'Ah, ah, ha, ha, ha,' I'd never seen him so scared and for the life of me I couldn't stop laughing. My sides were sore and I thought I was going to wet myself.

'I'm not a fruit, Eddie, honest I'm not. I was dreaming about Maria and me on the banks of the Colebrooke River and I, I, I must have, ha, ha, ha … got carried away … I'm sor, sor, sorry, ah, ha, ha, ha.'

Eddie was getting dressed in a hurry.

'Fuck this,' he raged. 'I'm away downstairs and if you

ever pull a stunt like that ever again, ever, I'll kill you.'

Now I knew he was really one hundred per cent serious and my laughter trickled to a halt. I threw my feet onto the floor and he stared in terror in the direction of my protruding underpants in the belief I was going to make a go for him.

'For God's sake settle down,' I laughed, 'I'm no fruit. Hold on till I get dressed and we'll go downstairs.'

The Three Telephones

It was 8.45 pm exactly when we entered the living room. Mrs Connolly was sitting in front of a roaring fire, deep in conversation with a lovely lady also in her early fifties, who was wearing a leopard skin, patterned mini-dress and gold, sling back high heeled shoes.

'Hello boys. I'd like to introduce you to Penelope, my neighbour. Bobbie and Eddie, meet Penelope.'

'A great country you have here, Penelope,' said Eddie, shaking hands and adding, 'we didn't realise Birmingham was as big as it is.'

'And I'm pleased to meet you Penelope. Are there any folk clubs in the area?' I asked, with an eye to getting some work.

'I think they hold them in Digbeth Town Hall. You could go down on the bus tomorrow and make some enquiries,' she replied.

'Thank you very much. We'll do that, won't we Eddie?'

He was still simmering from his encounter upstairs and mumbled dryly, 'aye'.

'Would you both like to come over to my house on your ceili?' smiled Penelope.

'We would indeed. Can we bring our guitars for a bit of a sing-song?'

'Of course you may. Please follow me. I'll be seeing you tomorrow Nora and by the way, thanks for the tea.'

'Not at all, Penelope, see you then.'

What friendly people, I thought.

Penelope was now walking very fast and her only words were, 'follow me'. Within seconds Nora had shut and locked the back door behind us and we entered a maze of dark, narrow, red-bricked alleys, which seemed to be forever turning left. Her pace dulled my sense of direction and at one point I wondered if this was intentional.

'Please come in boys and go straight into the lounge,' she directed, closing the backdoor and locking it firmly behind us.

The room was warm and spacious with wall-to-wall carpet, something we'd never walked on before. Leopard skin rugs hung from the walls and a bamboo curtain on the far right led to darkness.

Two girls sat on a long loose-covered sofa. They were the most beautiful I had ever seen, especially the one with short dark hair and skin that had never seen the sun. Her white blouse left little to the imagination, bulging and stretching and minus two buttons, but she didn't seem to notice. Her teeth were the finest ever God put into the head of a human being. Every time she smiled, which was often, her habit of grinding and crunching them together made my skin creep.

'Bobbie and Eddie, meet Sharon and Ziggie.'

'Hello girls,' we echoed and shook hands.

Penelope left us sitting opposite Sharon and Ziggie the way I wanted it. She took up her position behind a stout mahogany desk, which sat isolated in the centre of the floor. Three identical brass cradle telephones nestled in front of her, as did a notebook, a pen, an ashtray and a silver cigarette lighter made in the shape of a Buddha. A constant series of perfect smoke rings gave her an aura of anticipation and I marvelled at how she blew them without the slightest appearance of effort.

The phone rang and she lifted the middle one.

'Hello, yes, that is the 2.15 at Chepstow,' and she hung up.

Within minutes, another call came through and this time her message was almost the same.

'Hello, yes, that would be the 3 o'clock at Uttoxeter,' and she replaced the receiver.

'Riinngg! Burrr!'

'Hello, yes that will be the 4 o'clock at Newmarket,' and yet again the brass handset was placed on the matching cradle.

'Eddie' I whispered, putting my hand to the side of my mouth just in case the girls could lip-read, 'It's a bookies, this is a bookie's shop.'

'Bookie's shop my arse! It's a kip-shop. She's taking down bookings for the girls.'

'Christ! Let's go, we'll go back to the digs.'

'No, not yet. Let's see what happens, we're in no rush.'

'Do you know any songs, girls?' I asked, lifting my

guitar and trying hard to steady my nerves.

They looked at each other and giggled and then back at us.

'What will we give them?' Eddie asked as we tuned up.

'*Brennan on the Moor,* that's a good one. Willie Brennan was an Irish outlaw girls, who robbed the rich to feed the poor and naturally kept something for himself every now and again. He was like your own Robin Hood or Dick Turpin who rode Black Bess.'

They shook their heads in puzzlement before breaking into raucous laughter. I knew then that they had no interest whatsoever in English history.

'Oh it's of a brave young highwayman this story I will tell

His name was Willie Brennan and in Ireland he did dwell,

It was on the Kilworth Mountains he commenced his wild career

And many's the wealthy nobleman before him shook with fear.

And it's Brennan on the Moor, Brennan on the Moor,

Bold, brave and undaunted was young Brennan on the Moor.'

For over an hour they listened to us intently, applauding generously after every song and the telephone never stopped. Penelope got up from her table with the phones still ringing and approached us with a few lonely handclaps.

'Well done boys, well done. Now, how about taking

a little rest and I'll prepare a few drinks. What would you like?'

'Believe it or not, Penelope, I've never had a drink in my life but I think now's the time to start. My friend Joe Dixon back in Brookeborough told me if I ever started…'

Eddie interrupts.

'I've heard this story before and I don't feel like hearing it again. What he's trying to say Penelope is, he would like a Bacardi and coke and the same goes for me as well.'

'Bacardi and coke coming up. And the same for you girls?'

Once again they smiled and nodded and Sharon continued crunching and grinding. She was getting louder by the minute, reaching almost eight on the Richter scale.

After some time knocking back the Bacardis, I found myself sitting beside Sharon and opposite Eddie and Ziggie, though I couldn't figure out how I got there. Penelope was back on the phones, reciting race meetings and drinking and smoking her head off.

Two lonely guitars lay silently propped against the wall and we found ourselves deep in conversation with our new found friends.

'Sharon, were you ever over in Ireland?'

'No, but I'd like to go sometime. I've met so many nice people from there. Although I was born in Birmingham over in Sparkhill, my mother came from County Kerry.'

'I knew it! I knew it!' I said with gleeful excitement. 'The minute I set eyes on you, I knew you were one of us. It's funny, isn't it, how we always know our own? What do you do for a hobby?'

'I talk to wild Irishmen like you,' she smiled with a deep crunch on her molars.

'You're right Sharon, talking's the best medicine. My mother always said that, but we've heard the people over here wouldn't bid each other the time of day.'

'That's true, but anytime you feel like talking come and see me. I'm a good listener.'

'Jesus, Sharon, that's wild friendly of you. Thanks for being such a good neighbour.'

I could still see her as clear as day, but every now and then she blurred slightly and I reckoned this was just a normal part of my new experience with the drink.

'You're the loveliest girl I've ever seen.'

She seemed dumbstruck at my suggestion and ground her teeth once again.

'You're really very beautiful. I've never seen nicer than you,' I added.

I wondered what my Da would say if he saw me now. He'd probably shake that old white head of his in defeat once again and my Ma would pull me out by the ear and bring me to the priest. I was glad they were living and couldn't see me. If they were dead they could and then I'd be in trouble.

'Would you like to come and see my room?' she indicated, with dark, brown eyes aimed in the direction of the bamboo curtain. Checking the time on her slim, gold wrist-watch she got to her feet and walked across the floor in front of me.'

'Cheerio, Eddie, see you later. Sharon's going to show me her room.'

'Behave yourself and no fruitin',' he laughed.

'What the fuck do you mean? You bog hopper,' I snapped, pretending not to understand.

'Don't be going onto the banks of the Colebrooke,' he cheered.

The phones were now ringing two at a time.

'Don't listen to him Sharon. He's one ignorant, culchie fucker. His mother even married a Protestant.'

Once again she smiled broadly with a crisp crunch of immaculate teeth. I was quaking in my shoes as I followed her through the dangling slits of bamboo and waited as the flick of a well-polished fingernail surged the hall into a soothing block of crimson. The bulb oozed tranquillity, something I'd never experienced before and it made me think that one of these would be a necessity should I ever return to Brookeborough.

At the top of the stairs, the long corridor was centrepoint to the many rooms running off to the left and right, all with their doors open and bathed in that same red glimmer. Waiting.

Producing a key from deep within her blouse, she opened the glossiest, black door, standing aside while I entered and clicking the Yale lock behind me. I couldn't believe my eyes. The carpet, walls, roof, furniture, bed and even the counterpane were black. Everything was black, and the glow from the isolated red bulb made little impression.

'Would you like to take your clothes off? I'm taking mine off,' she said in a matter of fact kind of way, rasping her teeth with a vengeance.

'Well Sharon, the only time I take my clothes off is when I'm going to bed. That's the only time we take our clothes off in Ireland.'

'Come here,' she laughed, now as naked as the day she was born.

'Come where?' I answered, fighting for every second of time I could plunder.

'Bobbie, come to me.'

I liked her gentle, unrushed way of doing things. Her movements were slow, relaxed and deliberate and her voice almost narcotic in a way my Bacardi haze could appreciate.

The black butterfly tattoo, tucked neatly behind her right shoulder, was a work of art and said 'touch me' in four different languages. I only understood the English version but was too scared to follow instructions.

Her lips feathered my face and busy fingers began to open every button I owned.

'Sharon, I've never done this before – well, not like this, in a place like this. I'm powerful nervous. I think I'll go back to the digs.'

I watched her turn and take the few, short steps to the wardrobe where she reached up, produced a small bottle of tablets, shook two free and put it back again.

'Here, take these. Wash them down with this.'

'What are they?'

'Only aspros but you'll find they work well with Barcadi. Go on, take them and you'll see. Drink it up.'

'Aspros! Do you know something? My mother wouldn't be without them.'

'Shush! Come and rest.'

As the black counterpane peeled back, I climbed in and she followed. The second my head hit the pillow, I saw something and closed my eyes, but no matter how tight I closed them, it stayed there so I opened them again. Three massive, yellow bulldozers in battle line formation, rumbled and splashed towards me. Their drivers wore hurried smiles, as the water lapped the spinning track tops. A sign post read 'The Irish Sea'.

'Jesus!' I gulped, 'bulldozers on the Irish Sea, how do they do that? Sharon! Look up, they're beautiful. Can you see them? They're brilliant. They're racing fast but not moving. The sound's in the wrong place. They sound like they're on land but they're ploughing up the Irish Sea and flying tricolours. Look! Ah, ha, Jesus – the one on the right's sinking and the driver is jumping out – Look! He's jumped into the next one – phew! That was close. He was lucky there. What a brilliant jump. Look! He's waving at us. Christ! The second one's sinking and the two of them have jumped, ah, ha, ha, ha, ha, ha.'

Now, there was only one bulldozer left on the Irish Sea and it had three drivers. How could these iron elephants stay up for so long?

'Sharon! Would you look at that? The last one's

sinking. The cab is filling up. The sky is red. Everything's red. Why is that?'

'Easy. You can see anything, everything, if you want to,' she answered quietly.

'Jesus, I think I'm dying, Sharon. For fuck's sake keep your head down. Quick! Duck! Jesus, that was close.'

The lampshade's mouth smiled a twisted evil smile and stuck its tongue out at me. Then it melted, transforming itself into a cow's head with drilling horns.

'Don't look now Sharon. The cow's head's right behind you. Aw, Jesus, this is the end of the world. Put on the light, please turn on the white light.'

Her voice droned, 'there is no white light here, only red, red – red – red… The echo bounced off invisible walls, as the Sacred Heart picture from my bedroom in Brookeborough hovered above me in the blackness, dumping spats of dark blood, like treacle slush, all over my eyes and face.

'Sharon, whatever you do, don't look up. Your hair is covered in black, sticky blood. You have murdered me. I'm dead. It's God. He's here to take us away.'

'It's OK. I'm here baby. I won't let it harm you.'

Her teeth gleamed and crunched but I couldn't hear them any more. My ears crackled and sizzled with the silence as she lunged upwards and sat over me. It must have been two hundred degrees Fahrenheit in that room. The holy picture did a backward summersault and cart-wheeled into infinity as the dancing lampshade returned to twirling and darting through every inch of darkness. Settling on her head, it started to imitate a Christmas tree, blinking on and off before flashing blood-shot eyes and zooming away. Then something clicked and my hearing was switched on again. The muffled feet of a thousand horses galloped through my head and I thought it was going to explode. I was so thirsty.

'Sharon, it's going away. The red light is steady again.'

'Easy baby, I told you. It won't be long now.'

I could feel her tongue stabbing and panting, sweat teemed from my skin onto the fine silk sheets and slowly turned to ice, but her thawing warmth fought back and snuggled away my coldness. There was no doubt about it. She was the 1.15 at Uttoxeter, with the going good and getting good to hard in places. I'd swear Eddie heard us crossing the finishing line, where the judges ruled a photo-finish. I lay in her arms until the 1.45 at Chepstow and we fell asleep.

When I next looked at my watch, it was six o'clock and the city was coming to life again. The clatter of milk bottles on front doorsteps reminded me of home and how I used to jump over them on my way to school but that was long ago.

'Good morning, Sharon. Wake up! It's six.'

'Good morning Irish. Give me a kiss and a cigarette, in that order.'

Pulling deeply on the first smoke of the day, she asked, 'Bobbie, was that your first time?'

'Aye, you're good crack. Was that my first time?' I blustered, 'how did I do?'

'You were beautiful. It was your first time, wasn't it?'

'What age are you, Sharon?'

'I'm twenty-eight.'

'You look younger, I'm twenty.'

'And you look it,' she laughed.

'I've no money, only what I've got for the digs. Tell me what I owe you and when I get work I'll drop it round.'

She kissed my cheek and whispered, 'I don't want your money. Next time you call ask for me and only me. Just ask for Butterfly. Then I'll take your money if you have it.'

'Can I tell you I love you, Butterfly?'

'You can tell me anything, baby.'

'I like you an awful lot.'

'That's much better. It was your first time, wasn't it?'

A year or so later, I left Birmingham and returned home. Sharon and I kept in touch by letter and we became good friends. In October 1966 I travelled from Brookeborough and met her at the airport and for some inexplicable reason we ended up in Ardglass, County Down. On the bus she gave me a present of the works of Oscar Wilde signed 'to Irish from a good friend'.

Our stay in Donnan's Hotel in this most beautiful of fishing villages saw us up and sitting on the rocks at 6 am. My choice of place was a coincidence, for although I lived a hundred miles from Ardglass across in the west of Northern Ireland and had never been there before, in one month's time I would begin life as a mental nurse in Downshire Hospital just five miles away.

The News of the World

Every Sunday morning on the 'deeply disturbed' ward, one anxious solitary patient paced up and down, staring at the big, main door with unbelievable anticipation. The remaining twenty-nine sat on green, plastic-covered chairs, some of which had white, uneven cubes of foam rubber sticking out of them.

This was my favourite ward to work in. The patients were mobile and had good personal hygiene. From Monday to Friday they worked in Male Four gardens, cutting sticks, weeding, digging and generally doing the things everyone does in their own garden. In exchange for their work, which was also good therapy, they received tuck money to spend in the hospital shop.

Any moment now, that big, heavy door, strongly reinforced with Georgian wire glass would reverberate to the sound of Charlie's fist banging for admission. As regular as clockwork he delivered the papers and his timing was said to be more accurate than Big Ben's. Old Jimmy was pacing faster now, twisting his wrist and looking at it closely even though he didn't own a watch. His anxiety was at bursting point. I didn't need to take his pulse because I knew it would be way on the wrong side of a hundred and well above the 'normal' rate of seventy-two beats per minute.

The ward clock showed ten o'clock exactly and as the second hand swept the twelve, the echo of the door being thumped shook every corner of the day room, boot store, dormitory and washroom. Charlie had arrived and Jimmy was already on the spot gazing through the glass at him.

'Keys, Nurse! Keys, Nurse! Keys, Nurse!' roared Jimmy, 'Door! Door! Door!'

As soon as I had turned the lock, Jimmy reached out and grabbed the Sunday papers from Charlie. The *Sunday News, The Sunday Press, The Sunday Independent* and *The Sunday Times* were all thrown carelessly on the day room table, but Jimmy's favourite, *The News of the World,* was lovingly folded and placed under his left arm as he slowly strolled to his chair, which occupied the middle space in a long row below the windows.

It took me over a month to discover what Jimmy was up to, because senior nurses at that time believed that students' training would be more efficient if they learned to diagnose for themselves the peculiarities and mannerisms associated with the different types of mental illnesses. Jimmy's nose was much bigger than mine; red and swollen, with countless little capillaries criss-crossing it at every opportunity, giving the impression he had been a whiskey drinker, which he wasn't.

'Nurse Hanvey, Jimmy's only a cunt and you're a big silly cunt too, Nurse'.

'I know, John Joseph, I know'.

John Joseph hated the ward to be tranquil and you could bet money on him raring up as soon as all the patients were seated comfortably.

For over a month of Sundays, I had passed Jimmy as he read the paper and something in the back of my mind told me that things weren't quite as they seemed. I figured he just wasn't reading the paper correctly, so I decided to sit down and engage in a little discreet detective work. Sitting opposite him I could see the big broad sheet covering the upper half of his body. All that remained visible were his two knees, legs and immaculately polished boots, with the front and back pages reflecting on his carefully buffed toecaps.

'Your bum's a plum, Nurse. Your bum's a fuckin' plum.' John Joseph was at it again. Things were just too peaceful for him.

'Nurse, shut him up, the illiterate bastard,' said a voice from deep within *The News of the World*. John Joseph was interrupting Jimmy's reading and he did not like it one little bit. This was the spark that lit the bonfire. Now a babble of voices all aimed at John Joseph gained volume and intensity.

'Shut the silly bastard up!'

'He's only silly!'

'He's very silly!'

'Stick the big needle in his arse, Nurse!'

'Kill him, Nurse!'

All this aggression was too much for old Bertie the Butt, who was taking it all in but decided there was too much talk and not enough action. He stood upright on his chair and took deadly aim at John Joseph who was still stirring up the crowd. He roared at the top of his voice and assumed the pose for which he was famous - the aeroplane! Though a man of sixty-five, he moved like a tank only faster, and I knew there was no way I could stop the rapidly unfolding series of events already in motion.

John Joseph had his back to the Butt and was so involved in disturbing the ward, it would take a miracle at the very least to engineer his escape. He was standing in the middle of the 'runway' and 'the big 707 was set to go!' The goldfish tank was positioned at waist level on the dividing partition that separated the day room from the door area, only two feet from John Joseph and directly in front of him.

The Butt thundered across the ward, head down, eyes closed and arms outstretched, but beautifully on course and gaining speed by the second! I knew what was going to happen was inevitable and I stood up. So did the rest of the patients. They were cheering and shouting and baying for blood, but John Joseph never moved. Whack!

The Butt's head buried itself deeply into the small of John Joseph's back, catapulting him right through the fish tank, which immediately disintegrated. Water, rocks, algae, electric wire and fish were scattered here, there and everywhere. The ward was in shambles. A dozen nurses in long, white coats from adjoining wards, quickly arrived as back-up, just in case the violence spread – though, in stark contrast to similar scenes in the outside world, it never did.

The Butt, who had the strength of ten men, was gently restrained and held face down on the floor. An injection of Paraldehyde, a foul-smelling, almost instantaneous sedative, was quickly driven into his already bare right buttock. As far as the Butt was concerned, the war was over. Paraldehyde is secreted from the body through the skin and the lungs, giving off an odour similar to cat's piss. He wouldn't smell too pretty for a day or two!

Domestic staff flew into action with mops, brushes and small shovels, lifting every fragment of debris in sight. Then I noticed something very peculiar. The little goldfish, dozens of them, were no longer wriggling on the rubber-surfaced floor. They had vanished. I went over to a domestic and asked 'where did the fish go? Did you see any fish?'

'No, I didn't, come to think of it.' She turned to her mate, 'Did you see any fish, Doris?'

'No, there's no fish here,' replied Doris.

I scanned the faces around the room and I couldn't believe my eyes. Big Davy was hunched in his chair in the corner with the peak of his chequered cap pulled down over the tip of his nose, giving him some limited cover, chewing for all he was worth.

'Stand up, Davy,' I said.

The shining orange tail of a goldfish poked out between his lips, as he kept on munching, his mouth full to the teeth.

'Davy, I think you're eating the goldfish.'

'Go to Hell, I'm eating no fuckin' goldfish,' he mumbled. His words found great difficulty in making their way past such a mess of wanton destruction.

'Empty your pockets please, Davy.'

He did as I ordered and one, two, six, ten, fourteen trembling tiddlers showered to the floor. I told him to go and change his coat.

John Joseph, meanwhile, was up and about again without a scratch. He had not come into contact with the water at all and was as dry as a bone. All the aggro had disappeared and as quiet as a mouse he waltzed across the room. Through all this commotion, Jimmy continued reading the newspaper as though nothing had happened.

'I want the paper, Nurse! I want the paper!' cried John Joseph.

So much for 'the aeroplane', I thought.

'Get me the paper or I'll wreck the fuckin' ward.' I knew he wouldn't.

'He's not getting it,' bellowed Jimmy. 'Sure, the wee fucker's illiterate. He's getting no paper, it's mine.'

'It's not, it's not, it's the ward's,' shouted John Joseph.

The paper sat motionless, like a silent sail on a glassy sea. It was my main focus of attention. When people read newspapers they make noise. They turn and rattle pages and shake the sheets to fold them over. But not Jimmy, he was sitting like a model in a waxworks museum.

All of a sudden, an most almighty roar lanced my eardrums as John Joseph rocketed three feet into the air and landed squarely on the broad of his back, with blood pumping from a gash in the back of his head. His face was alive with twitches and froth and spittle had combined and flowed ever so slowly from the corner of his mouth. His eyes rolled as if searching for direction and his body shook uncontrollably all over. He had also wet himself.

I checked to see if he had bitten or swallowed his tongue and made sure his airway was clear. He was OK. All the patients had gathered round in a circle as if witnessing the scene of a traffic accident.

'Move back and give him air,' ordered the Charge Nurse. Everyone took one pace backwards, widening the circle.

'He's dead,' said one.

'No, not yet,' diagnosed another.

'Get the doctor. Get the priest. Get the undertaker,' they all shouted. Then out of all the bedlam a lone steady voice of reason calmly stated, 'It's only a fit'. It was that voice from behind The News of the World again.

John Joseph was carried to bed in the dormitory to sleep it off. Tomorrow, he would be back to his old tricks. Everything in the ward was peaceful again. It was so quiet you could hear a body drop!

The paper opposite developed a steady tremble and I crept from my chair to investigate.

'The Nurse's up!' shouted Peter, who was known as 'the early warning system' because he had saved more lives in the hospital than anyone else. When fires broke out, or when pipes burst, or if patients were in difficulty, he was the first to let the staff know. He had been traumatised during World War Two, but his upper crust English accent was a source of tranquillity and added a little class to the ward. If the hospital was being demolished by a series of explosions Peter would more than likely approach you calmly and say, 'Excuse me, Nurse, there's a series of explosions going off'.

He was as cool as death. Jimmy never budged. I sat down again, just in case he spotted me.

'Nurse's down again,' reported Peter, loudly.

'I'll sicken you, Peter,' I said to myself, as I began standing up and sitting down in rapid succession.

'Nurse's up. Nurse's down. Nurse's up. Nurse's down,' repeated Peter, as I finally collapsed back into my chair.

'Nurse is now seated sensibly,' he added.

Peter never missed a trick and if he never missed a trick he would surely know what Jimmy was up to behind the paper. After all, he had been watching him for years. I walked over towards him.

'Nurse is approaching from north-north-west. Nurse has now arrived and is sitting down. Good morning Nurse and how are we today? I've just been enjoying forty winks,' he said in his rich officer's accent.

'Peter, could you tell me one thing?' I whispered.

'Most certainly Nurse, let me have it.'

'What is Jimmy doing behind that newspaper?'

'It's very simple old boy. You don't have to be a constable to figure that one out.'

By now I was twenty feet away from Jimmy, this time

seeing him in three-quarters profile.

'Watch his left hand,' said Peter, 'that chap Jimmy is left-handed - do you follow so far, Nurse?'

'Yes, I do.'

'Do you see his pocket move Nurse? Now tell me what you see.'

'He's interfering with himself, that's what he's doing.'

'Masturbating, old chap, always stick rigidly to the English language and don't be afraid to call a spade a spade. Now, go over and see what page he's at and watch out for his nose.'

'His nose?' I questioned.

'Yes, his nose, don't forget his nose,' said Peter.

Tiptoeing up beside Jimmy I noticed the pocket was still moving and sure enough the page revealed a big photograph of an unusually healthy looking girl with big breasts, sitting on a bale of hay. Without a doubt, this picture was aimed fairly squarely at the male members of the farming community, because right beside her and slightly to the left, sat a big Ferguson tractor. A few pitchforks and shovels lay against a sheet of corrugated iron, helping to complete the illusion of a peaceful rustic scene.

'You're masturbating, Jimmy,' I ventured.

'I'm not, I'm not fuckin' wankin',' he responded angrily, as The News of the World trembled uncontrollably.

'What happened to your nose, Jimmy?' I asked.

'There's nothing wrong with my fuckin' nose,' he snapped. 'Go away to the mirror and look at your own nose and give my head peace.' The tip of his nose was as black and shiny as his boots. The editor and photographers of that most popular of 'Sunday's' never failed to deliver the goods, and supplied the bould Jimmy with a new girl every week. She was never late. She always arrived at ten on the dot.

I wet my finger on my tongue and touched his nose to see if the black stuff would come off, and sure enough it did. Jimmy jerked his head to the side in disgust.

'It's black newsprint,' confirmed Peter. He was right again. Jimmy had been kissing the photograph.

'Nurse is turning now. Nurse is walking across the floor - this time, south, south-west. Nurse is sitting down.'

'Well! What a morning!' There was never a dull moment on the deeply disturbed ward.

The Graveyard Shift

The nurses' night station was an isolated affair, a splash of calming light in the middle of a sprawling oasis, giving a fair view of the fifty beds to all sides of that simple table and chair. A couple of daily newspapers already ravaged by the previous two shifts, lay curled and combined with half-finished crossword puzzles begging for completion. This period of duty from 9.30 pm to 7 am was known in the profession as 'the graveyard shift'.

Once the patients were in bed for the night, you could be fairly certain that things would remain peaceful for another four hours. In most wards, night duty simply amounted to the art of staying awake, but in the psycho-geriatric units things were never so predictable. It was touch and go. Vomiting, diarrhoea and nightmares were only some of the complaints that could wake one patient who in turn would disturb every other sleeper in the house. Night after night, an uneventful shift hung in the balance and tranquillity rested in the lap of one sleeping man.

Born in 1877, old Archie had recently celebrated his ninety-first birthday. As a young man who fought in the Boer War, he had the unique habit of referring to members of the nursing staff as 'kaffir'. He had been admitted to the Downshire in 1922, when it was known as the Down Lunatic Asylum and must have witnessed many changes down through the years, but maybe hadn't even noticed. His bed was the middle one in a row of five. Archie had good personal hygiene, was a sound sleeper from dark to daylight, and his bed one of the few to remain in pristine condition.

Then, in the winter of 1967, things started to go wrong for Archie. His sheets began to take on a new dimension – they were marked with faeces, although his nightshirt always looked as if it was fresh out of the linen press.

'You've dirtied your bed again, Archie,' Sean, the Staff Nurse told him.

'No I did not soil my bed, kaffir, honestly, I did not. Shake hands kaffir, no hard feelings.'

As my hand advanced, long-nailed fingers and a thumb clamped my wrist and locked like a pair of pincers.

'Ah Jesus! Get him off me Sean,' I pleaded.

'That'll teach you to take old age for granted,' he laughed. 'This time he didn't draw blood. Next time you mightn't be so lucky.'

'How does he manage to dirty his bed and keep his night-shirt clean?' I asked.

'He simply pulls it up, does what he has to and pulls it down again. Right! Let's get him changed or we'll not get sitting down tonight. I've had a rough day. Get him out.'

'OK Archie. Out you come – onto this seat. Look at that dirt in your bed.'

'It's not my dirt, honest kaffir. It's them hens. They were in again last night. I heard them cackling.'

After a week or more of changing his bed linen, I decided to pay him a little more attention. The next night at 2 am I checked his bed. It was dry and clean. So far so good. Three o'clock. He was still sound asleep and all was well. Four thirty. Dirty again, in exactly the same place and as usual his white cotton nightshirt was spotless.

'It's them hens kaffir. They were in again last night, hundreds of them. Did you not see them, kaffir?'

'No, Archie, I did not.'

The following night at two o'clock, I was pretending to read the paper but kept one eye on the bay and the other on two down and seven across. At five to three wee Robert in the bed beside Archie's, pulled back his blankets and with spindly legs dangling over the edge, stood up on the floor and gawked all around him. His bald head punched the stale air, as ferret eyes cut through the dimness and fixed themselves on the night station and me. Through the roughly cut out hole in page one, I observed him. A voice from the ocean of snores cried out, 'Mammy, Mammy, Mammy, put on the tay pot, Mammy,' and the ward went quiet again. Wee Robert flicked his gaze in the direction of the toilet which had a constant hiss of refilling cisterns. He shuffled silently in hurried slowness, unable to generate the momentum needed to get him there sooner. Within minutes, the bony scuff of bare-feet told me he was returning and I watched as he pulled back the bedclothes and climbed in.

I supposed Ma and Da were fast asleep by now up in old Brookeborough. I'm sure the inhabitants of the entire village were snoring their heads off, their nightly rituals of hugs, turning backs, acrobatics and I love youse far behind them and long forgotten. Once every year, someone died there. I hoped it wasn't tonight. I scanned the crossword - eleven letters in three groups 4-2-5. Name the capital of Haiti. 'Papa Doc, the Ton Ton Macoute, yes, Port-au-Prince'.

Lowering the paper to nose level, I looked over it and experienced something so fascinating that I asked my self why this 'magic' had previously eluded me. A ghostly orchestra of rumbling sound reached out to invade my soul. It was all there, with not one single ingredient missing - everything from trembling bass to the high-pitched whistle of a boiling kettle. No two the same. Like fingerprints, all unique to their owners. A pit stop of flippered lips ticking over as beautifully as finely tuned engines during Le Mans. A legion of snores.

'What the fuck's he at? How did I miss that?'

Wee Robert's blankets were pulled back again. Dropping the paper on the table, I walked the ten steps to his bed and looked under it. Nothing. He was gone. Old Archie was sound asleep and probably dreaming of Mafeking. I'd checked his bed to make sure he was comfortable. Slowly peeling back the sheets, I couldn't believe my eyes. Archie was lying on his side with his back to me as Wee Robert's eyes shone up from the blackness, like beacons from a distant lighthouse. His nightshirt was pulled up around his waist. I had found the culprit.

'Right! Robert! Out to the toilet and don't let me catch you in here again.'

Sean, who sat at another table twenty yards away, rushed over to lend a hand. On Sunday afternoons during visiting, Robert was never able to recognise his wife or family but the guilt presently written all over his face told me something that was impossible to understand.

'Archie! Wake up!' called the Staff Nurse.

'You're bed's in an awful mess,' I added.

'The warning shots were fired, kaffir, as we tries to cross the Modder. Then the hens came in. They were in again last night kaffir.'

His voice was slow and feeble as it had always been but I could sense a slight sprinkling of fear coming through.

'I heard them coming. If you don't believe me ask General Buller, kaffir. Cluck, cluck, cluck, cluck! Aaagh! Take your filthy hands off me, kaffir,' he shrugged with a fierce bellow, as a fat fist skimmed my chin and the noise he made spilled out and wakened patients in domino fashion.

'Shut your mouth you dirty dog.'

'Fuck up you shameless sow.'

'The poor wee donkey, feed the donkey, Johnny.'

Voices from everywhere came slicing down, as old Felix sang Jingle Bells and the very few who could remember it, joined in. Soon, every bed in the ward would have to be changed and that would take hours.

'Come on Archie. Out till we change you sheets. You can keep watch by the river.'

'Kindly pass my rifle, kaffir.'

I handed him his imaginary rifle, which he loaded and took aim.

'We're moving on to Ladysmith, kaffir. They're on the banks of the Tugela, millions of the bastards.'

As we swopped fresh linen for soiled, I watched his tired old eyes dance and sparkle. When things settled down, I read his case history to determine the cause of his illness. The notes said shellshock. Archie may have been shell-shocked but as far as the hens were concerned he was almost right.

January 1967

The patients were all tucked up and counted - all fifty of them. The last round was done. Dirty sheets in the psycho-geriatric ward were quickly disposed of. Old men had been washed and made as comfortable as possible and the yellow glow from the ward's night light transformed bedlam into a new world, totally at ease with itself.

The constant hum from the air conditioning combined beautifully with the wall-to-wall ripple of snoring contentment. Sporadic bouts of bad language guaranteed the more persistent hecklers at least another small measure of Largactil before the sweet cloud of peace finally descended for the night. Every evening the pattern was the same.

Half nine ended my late shift and, after pulling off a brilliant white, knee-length coat (white that is, except for the scattered brown marks of 'collision' here and there), I would quickly wash my hands and face in the cloakroom and call it a day.

I had no way of knowing my life would begin in January 1967 and headed back through the ward for the solitude of the nurses' home. The air-conditioning pressed louder on my eardrums, as I saw a tall, slim figure dressed in the smart, blue uniform of a student nurse step quietly out of the darkness, some six beds away. The locker mirror to her right cast a perfect profile, with neatly groomed fair hair and white starched paper hat. I remember thinking with disbelief how strange to appear so beautiful and yet quite plain at the same time. Her very being radiated a joy with life that I had never encountered before.

To see her image in that low, half light reminded me of a picture my mother treasured at home - the simple, yet lingering beauty of the Blessed Virgin Mary, always dressed in blue and held in the highest regard possible, above all the saints, his Holiness the Pope and even John F. Kennedy.

In those days, whenever a girl looked at me I saw myself through her eyes. Confidence was easy then. In that haunting half darkness, her eyes cut into mine with that beautiful, despairing hopelessness of coming death, but the barely visible tremble of lips revealed a young girl shaking with innocent caution on the verge of womanhood. A white confident hand slid quietly from behind her apron top.

Jesus, she sure has some spirit, I thought, as she stood on the rubber-coated floor as if part of it. Fine, perfect fingers reached out in my direction, as highly polished regulation black shoes remained firmly on the spot. I walked to within arm's length and our hands locked. I was now as nervous as she was. Our eyes liked each other. They never blinked nor faltered as they absorbed what they saw. They ate each other with a great hunger. They were busy doing what only eyes can do best, but now and again in that short but never ending pause, they rested for a moment before becoming busy again. They were at their work and we knew it.

A great silence surrounded me as the drone from the air conditioning retreated and was gone. Nervous messages floated to and fro as our hands, still entwined in time, sweated in a constant ward temperature of eighty degrees.

'So, you're the great Bobbie Hanvey,' she said. 'I'm Maggie Maguire, student nurse, and I'm pleased to meet you.'

'And I'm pleased to meet you too, Maggie Maguire.' That was all it took.

Easter

After Mass in the Great Hall, which was used for games and recreation for the patients and for dances, concerts and films, we strolled the short distance to the Sugar Bowl, where patients and staff would socialise and drink tea.

'Father Murphy gave a beautiful sermon,' she enthused, as she tossed the usual two spoonfuls of sugar into my cup.

'He did indeed, but it was a pity Wee Tessie jumped up when she did. I think he was very embarrassed.'

'Sure, isn't she always doing things like that? I'm sure he paid no attention and hardly even noticed,' she said dismissively.

I doubted very much if Father Murphy hardly noticed, as the disruption came at the most important part of the Mass. Father Pat was just about to raise the Host and as everyone was kneeling down with their heads bowed and breath bated, Wee Tessie escaped from her seat and took a long mad run the full thirty yards up the aisle. She ground to a halt six steps short of the altar. One hundred heads turned like clockwork.

'Shoot her, Nurse!' cried a voice buried deep within

the congregation.

'Hanging's too good for her!' piped another.

'Pagan!' shouted a third.

Soon, dozens of highly charged, vitriolic comments were hurled in Tessie's direction, as she bounced into the air and landed flat on her face on the highly polished pine floor. With her arms and legs flailing up and down in an awkward, sprawling movement, she screamed, kicked and finally squealed, 'Father, would you exorcise me, Father? Exorcise me. The devil's in me. He's in me, Father! Do something quick… ahhhhh…' Caustic comments from the shocked gathering stopped abruptly.

Either Father Pat hadn't been trained in the finer points of an exorcism or the hierarchy believed there was a proper time and place for everything, but whatever the reason he slowly and respectfully raised the Host to a congregation suddenly oblivious as to their real reason for being there.

Tessie's screams intensified, drowning out the sharp, flurried rings of the Consecration Bell. Before the staff had time to muster and deliver the necessary restraint, Big Davy, who had stubbornly remained in the keeling position waiting for the bell, jumped to his feet and with fat, massive fists uppercutting the air, he thundered, 'Hit her a big kick in the arse Father! She's only a… imm! imm! imm!' Before Big Davy could complete this, the biggest line of his life, with the customary and automatic four letter word, a male nurse miraculously managed to muffle his mouth, with a well aimed right hand editing the sentence perfectly. Both Tessie and Davy were unceremoniously removed and taken back to their respective wards. Mass continued and ended without further interruption.

'Would you like to go for a walk, Maggie?' I said, smiling again at the thought of Mass.

'I'd like that,' she agreed, as we pushed our chairs underneath the table and once again tasted the half-chill of a beautiful Easter morning. Outside the Sugar Bowl, Old Harry was collecting freshly chucked butts from the ground and on spying us from the corner of his eye, immediately rushed over.

'Give us a butt Nurse. Come on, give us a butt. Have you got a fag Nurse? Go on, give us a cigarette. I know you've got them nurse. Give us one and I'll go away. Don't be so greedy Nurse. I know you've got plenty, for I see the packet in your pocket, Nurse. Give us a fag. Go on, give us a fag.'

'I don't smoke, Harry,' I replied.

'I know you smoke, I saw you and the Nurse smoking in the Sugar Bowl, you can't fool me,' he smiled, rubbing his hands together constantly in anticipation.

'Bobbie, would you please stop that and give him a cigarette', Maggie urged.

'Oh all right then, here's a fag, Harry.'

'Thanks, Nurse. Would you give me two? I have none for later.'

'OK, here's two.'

'Go on Nurse, give me three and I'll have one for tomorrow.'

'That's all you're getting, Harry. Now, away you go,' I said.

'Thanks Nurse, thanks Nurse.'

Turning to walk away, I heard him mumble under his breath, 'Nurse is only a fucker – a rotten fucker. He's rotten. He can stick his fags up his arse.'

As I looked at Maggie, she burst out laughing at the idea of Old Harry conning two fags as nicely as you've every seen.

'Do you believe I love you Maguire?'

'I do believe that.'

'Do you think it's possible I'll always love you?'

'I can think that as well,' she smiled.

As we walked through the tall trees, which looked magnificent by day but most sinister during the hours of darkness, I noticed small bits of twigs wafting earthwards. Careless crows, who were too busy for their own good, dropped piece after piece, all of which happily missed us and ended up crackling under-foot.

'Stop that! Stop that!' I shouted up at them.

'You're an eejit, but I love you, Hanvey.'

'I'm in the right place, but I'm glad you're here with me,' I replied.

'And the same goes for me too, Hanvey.'

Maggie took short, healthy puffs from a Benson and Hedges, held freely in slender fingers, as a gentle breeze barely touched our skin and prepared itself for a busy summer in the fields and streets of Ulster.

I kicked a loose stone in front of me. When Maggie came to where it rested, she kicked it also and at the

123

same time searched my eyes for approval, before turning her head and blowing more of those perfect, fluffy rings into the air. Her teeth laughed beautifully through thin, lifting smoke, until I could see her face clearly again.

As we entered the Lower Garden, the hospital towered above and behind us, so unbelievably big – majestic, commanding, immovable - but home to us nevertheless. We sat down on a row of haphazardly arranged cement blocks and I noticed a pair of black rosary beads snake slowly from my right trouser pocket and gradually find their way to the ground. I picked them up quickly and with gleeful excitement she remarked, 'I didn't think you were religious'.

'Now Maggie, a person's religion is a very private thing. But I suppose you're right. I'm not terribly religious, but my parents are. Just like you.'

She carefully examined every bead on every decade, with the delicacy of handling a butterfly, and asked, 'Where did you get them?'

'My father gave them to me before I left home to come here. He said they would keep me safe during life's journey and so far they've done that.'

'He's right,' she answered, as she looked deeply into my eyes as if trying to emphasise the fact.

A group of twenty patients, accompanied by a nurse, were approaching, dancing and singing their way down the steep pathway that was the other entrance to the garden. Donovan was doing his stuff on one of those small, tinny-sounding, transistor radios, as everyone joined in, in perfect time. The song was Mellow Yellow. The singing grew louder as it came closer, 'I'm just mad about Saffron and Saffron's mad about me.' On the word 'mad' they purposely raised the level of their voices and shouted it out really loud, to let us know they weren't quite so mad as some people would have liked to believe.

'Hello, Nurse Hanvey. Hello Nurse Maguire,' they called in a jumble, with one voice over-lapping the other, but Donovan sang on regardless.

'It's a lovely day, Nurse Hanvey' said Mary, who had been a patient in the Downshire for over forty years.

'Hello, Mary. It surely is.'

'Do you like my new lipstick, Nurse?' asked Bridget.

'Look at my new shoes, Nurse,' pointed Anne.

'Is Nurse Maguire and you getting married, Nurse Hanvey?' asked Dorothy. Before I could reply, she told me that she hadn't taken her medicine and she loved Donovan.

'We're going to Beach House for our summer holidays. It's great out there,' she bubbled.

'Where are you going now?' I enquired.

'To the Sugar Bowl,' was the united reply.

Ruth was also a long-stay patient, known throughout the hospital for her tremendous ability when it came to telling jokes. All of her yarns were in one way or another connected to the nursing profession, as if in some strange way this was her only means of striking back at a system that was kind to her but detained her against her will just the same.

'Would you like to hear a joke, Nurse?'

'I'd love to Ruth,'

'Right,' she smiled, 'Did you hear about the patient who walked into Doctor Dougal's office?' 'Dougal looked over his glasses and said, 'Young man, I'm afraid you're suffering from acute anxiety.' The patient replied, 'Dr Dougal … I'm afraid there's nuthin' cute about it.'

They all roared with uncontrollable laughter and moved away just as quickly as they had arrived, this time with Mick Jagger and the Rolling Stones belting it out across the airwaves. The song being sung had been doing the rounds for over a year and was especially popular within the confines of Downshire: 'Here it comes, here it comes, here comes my nineteenth nervous breakdown'.

Maggie was pulling her rosary in string-like movement from a warm, breast pocket, her finger and thumb gently trailing the silver crucifix upwards until the end loop leaped to freedom and crashed softly onto her creaseless uniformed lap. Carefully lifting them, I kissed the 'sign of the cross' and placing the crucifix against her lips, I kissed her. With only our knees touching, our eyes burned.

'Maggie Maguire, I'll always love you.'

'And I'll always love you too, Bobbie Hanvey.'

I took the two sets of rosary beads in both hands and mixed and jumbled them up, as a pipe-smoker might rub tobacco. I felt this procedure would copper-fasten our love forever.

The Day Trip

I had known a week earlier that the day trip to the seaside was on. This was one of the more enjoyable aspects of nursing, when patients and staff would leave the hospital in the early morning and seldom return before bedtime, which was usually around ten o'clock. It was a day when the nearest hotel would be invaded, confectionery and ice cream shops swamped, and a never-ending supply of cigarettes laid on free-of-charge by the hospital staff.

On the morning of departure, the atmosphere was electric. Patients who normally rose with a little encouragement at seven, had been washed and dressed and were walking up and down in anticipation from daybreak. Big Davy, the General, Mosie, Buns, the Butt and the Human Cannonball were a few of the boys preparing to make this the greatest day of their lives. Old Johnny Longstone sat expressionless in the chair below the budgies' cage gazing at a television still fast asleep, with no power and no programmes. His isolation was total in the midst of thirty empty chairs pointing in as many different directions, yet his frail, lonely reflection on that dull, grey screen probably told him a story of what might have been, had Lady Luck dealt him a kinder hand.

Johnny had worked in radio during the 1940s and 1950s. He had a career that most people would 'die' for - unlimited expense accounts, foreign travel, mixing with the rich and famous, and a beautiful home and family in Belfast's suburbia. This completed a fairy-tale lifestyle. When a classic interview with a well-known local clergyman went terribly wrong, he overnight gained the status of a 'persona non grata' and his talents were no longer required.

On the day of the ill-fated interview, as radio sets across the province warmed comfortable parlours with their vital weekly message, a dozy wasp suitably clad in its usual yellow and black striped pullover silently entered the studio. As with humans approaching the end of their life span, it seemed to spend more time walking than it did in flight. Tiptoeing at speed and sporting the customary hump on its back, this little fellow soon gained unnoticed admission to the inside of Johnny's open-necked shirt.

As the Holy Reverend led the praises of all the things which were good in life and commented on the beautiful summer weather presently being sponsored by the Lord Jesus Christ, Johnny roared 'FUCK IT' as the wasp's lethal injection buried itself deeply in his sun-tanned chest. Next day he was told to pack his bags and go. His days at the microphone were over.

'Old hands', who had been nursing for a lifetime and who remembered Johnny being admitted to Downshire, recalled him being a proper gentleman, soft spoken with an English accent, which was neither here nor there, but quite pleasant just the same. An outstanding conversationalist during his early days of hospitalisation, time saw him gradually regress to using monosyllables when his wife finally left him and her visits ceased. After that period of cascading traumas, all he would say to any question or suggestion was 'fuck it'. No other words ever crossed his lips, although he must have known thousands.

'It's a lovely morning, Johnny.'

'Fuck it,' was his only reply.

'Are you going to church today? The Reverend Brown is coming down from Belfast.' Without fail, each and every time, his answer was the same. He stood five foot four with a pencil-thin moustache and forever reminded me of the Scottish accordion player Jimmy Shand. Johnny had a nasty little habit of creeping up on patients and staff when they least expected it, before letting fly with a lethal, hatchet-sharp fist. Hit or miss he always added 'fuck it,' which had been his nickname for fifteen years.

Still, this year's trip would be transformed beyond recognition from anything experienced before and the boys were rarin' to go. For the first time in the Mental's long history, Male Forty-Seven would amalgamate with Female Thirty-Eight, just for the day. The patients agreed that this new programme of social interaction could only lead to better things. It was 8.20 am when the receptionist in the front hall telephoned the ward to inform us the excursion bus had arrived.

Big Cecil, the Charge Nurse, walked briskly from his office and stopped suddenly in the middle of the dayroom floor. Thirty pairs of anxious eyes were agog and gazing at him. Ties of every shape and colour had been tightened, shoes polished to an army shine, and Brylcreem-laden heads combed in every style imaginable.

'Right boys,' commanded Big Cecil, 'the bus is here, grab your things and let's go.'

A loud cheer went up and almost immediately died down again. Seconds later, a solitary voice cheeped 'fuck it'. It was Johnny, of course.

'Shut him up, Nurse,' bellowed Big Davy, 'his fuckin' language is desperate.'

'Hammer the bastard, choke him.'

'When are we getting our dinner,' stormed John Joseph, eager to get in on the act.

'Now John Joseph, you're only after your breakfast. Don't worry. You'll get your dinner in the big hotel.'

'What about my tea, Nurse? What about my tea? I need my tea,' he panicked.

'You'll get your tea too, John Joseph,' I assured him.

Twenty years earlier, when conditions in the Mental were more primitive and before science revolutionised treatment, Paul had been given a pre-frontal leucotomy. This was the worst cure imaginable for unpredictable behaviour. A drill, similar to the ones used in masonry, bored through the bone at the side of the temple and clinically sterilised medical instruments probed their way around the brain, cutting and removing the offending parts deemed responsible for irrationality. This procedure was known to sometimes kill the personality.

In Paul's case, it made him more loveable and docile but sharpened his already caustic sense of Ulster humour. His general demeanour was one of shell-like delicacy that gave the impression that if you should touch him he would disintegrate. After the operation, his hair never grew again and a deep dent on the side of his forehead was living proof of the point of entry. The pain he endured during convalescence was forever present and his description of the torment was graphically described in his horrific accounts of the events as he remembered them.

New student nurses, prompted by the older hands would ask, 'Paul, what happened to your head?' His answer never varied. The constancy of the same chilling string of words added to their authenticity and convinced us beyond any shadow of a doubt that what we heard was true. 'They shaved my head with a broken bottle and shoved a live dog up my arse,' was his condensed and teeth-rasping reply. As a description of pure, blue, naked pain, I have never heard a more flesh crawling account.

Paul was now standing in his full frame of five foot eight in front of me, smiling and winking with his left eye at irregular intervals.

'Give me a fag, Nurse,' he wheezed, as he proceeded to deliver a mild threat from an organisation which had lain dormant since 1962.

'I'm the Secretary of the IRA,' he warned, 'and if you don't give me a fag, I'll blow up your wife.'

'But I haven't got a wife, Jimmy,' I smiled.

'Then I'll blow up your mother,' he rattled.

'But my mother lives in County Fermanagh,' I smirked.

'It doesn't matter where she lives. If I manage to get the message out, she'll not be safe in China. I'm the Secretary of the Irish Republican Army. Do you know how much money we have in the bank?'

'No, Jimmy, I don't,'

'Four shillings and eleven pence,' he grinned.

'Here's a fag, Jimmy. The last thing this ward needs is an explosion. Now go with the rest of the boys to the bus.'

'Thanks Nurse, you're lucky this time. Let's hope your luck holds out,' he concluded, walking off with the cigarette clenched in narrow lips, collar turned up and hands dug deep in the pockets of the long overcoat that remained on him night and day. As far as being Secretary of the IRA was concerned, I wasn't so sure. There was no mention of it in his case notes, but from the way he spoke and swaggered, I suppose it could very well at one time have been possible.

Within a matter of minutes, all of the patients fell into line and were soon eagerly seated in the bus beside an equal number of female patients.

'I see you have a new girlfriend, Johnny,' sparked Joe Mulligan, a student nurse from County Tyrone. 'What would you do if you took her to the cinema?'

'Fuck it,' he responded, with a face void of any known emotion.

The bus was in uproar as the Charge Nurse and Ward Sister once again counted and checked heads and finally took their seats. The key in the ignition turned. The old engine, which had seen better days, spluttered and coughed and the big wheels started to roll. We were on our way to Portrush, County Antrim.

Still on the Bus

It was my luck to be seated beside Sister O'Flynn. She was in her mid-to-late forties, or so it appeared to me at the time.

Ward sisters had fearsome reputations and were looked upon by the junior nursing staff as being overbearing, frustrated and vicious. They ruled with an iron fist and their names were forever being discussed and repeated like a litany of terror. It wasn't good news to be notified you were being transferred to one of their wards and the fear of going there provided me with many sleepless nights.

'Good morning, Nurse Hanvey,' she said stiffly.

'Good morning, Sister O'Flynn.'

'You're making quite a name for yourself in Downshire.'

'Is that so, Sister,' I answered, wondering how much she'd heard about my antics and how much she disapproved. I didn't know a lot about introductions but I did know her approach was straight from the psychology textbook. If you want to put someone at ease when meeting them for the first time you simply say, 'Hello, I'm pleased to meet you. I have heard so many nice things about you.' On the other hand, if you want them to feel ill-at-ease your approach should be, 'Oh, hello, I've heard so many things about you.' They then begin to wonder what you've heard, if it was good or bad, and will probably go to the ends of the earth to find out what you do know and who told you. This was Sister's approach.

'I hear you're living in the nurses' home, Nurse Hanvey.'

'Yes, I like it there, Sister, it's so different from the County Fermanagh.'

'How is it different?'

'Well, in the Male Home I have a bath and hot water twenty-four hours a day. At home in Brookeborough I used to rig the garden hose up to the cold water tap in the scullery and pull it through the kitchen window out into the coal house. I'd throw the nozzle over a rafter and shower all summer long, but every time I'd take a shower, my problem was always the same. My feet and ankles were black and japped by the coal so I had to fill the basin and wash them all over again. Still those were great, happy days.

'The Male Home also has a fridge, which is never allowed to go empty. I never saw one before I came to Downshire. All we had was a larder - a little square green cage with tin sides, all drilled with thousands of tiny circular holes, just big enough to allow the air to circulate through and small enough to keep the flies out.'

'Yes, I remember them, we had one as well.'

'So there you are now, Sister. Now, you know what

I'm talking about, but I bet you never showered in the coal.'

She gave no answer.

I shouldn't have said that, I thought, and me supposed to show respect for authority.

'I'm sorry Sister. I shouldn't have said that.'

'And so you shouldn't, Nurse Hanvey,' she replied coldly, but immediately asked me what other facilities I found in the nurses' home.

'My bed linen is changed every week and I get two clean towels every day. There's a washing machine, a telephone, central heating and a television, although my father recently bought one of those. When my money runs out, Mr Sammy Stewart keeps me floating from his petty cash box in the Wages Office until pay day. If it wasn't for him, I couldn't afford to work here. We have a tennis court behind the home and a morgue to the side, so I think I have everything I need. Downshire's brilliant.'

'You mentioned the morgue,' she echoed curiously.

'Yes, I did.'

'Why did you mention the tennis court and the morgue in the same breath?'

'No special reason, Sister, they're almost beside each other, that's all.'

'Do you often go to post-mortems?' she bristled.

'As often as possible.'

'Why?' she demanded.

'Well, my mate Billy and I know when there's going to be one because we see the hearse passing by.'

'But why do you go?'

'Because it passes the time and anyway we enjoy seeing the female nurses fainting when the bodies are opened up,' I added warmly. 'Oh yes, we enjoy it all right.'

'Drownings, burnings, shootings, suicides, knifings, hangings, poisonings, road smashes, fallings from great heights. I think we've seen death from every cause and I suppose there's probably not much left to see.'

'Does it ever make you sick?'

'It did in the beginning, but it doesn't any more. I reckon you can get used to anything, Sister.'

Lighting a long cigarette, she briefly looked at me before glancing away again and adding, 'I'm not so sure about that'.

'Did you know, Sister, that Protestants and Catholics have one thing in common?'

'And that's what?' she asked, giving the impression that no known comparisons existed.

'They all go to Heaven with their heads full of *The Irish News.*'

'Please get to the point and explain yourself, Nurse Hanvey'.

'OK, Sister. As you know, the Morgue Attendant reads *The Irish News* and it's his job to prepare the body for the pathologist. After he removes all the major organs such as the heart and lungs and dissects them, it's the assistant's task to return them to the body. Usually they're poured into the cavity from a basin, but the brain, for whatever reason, is always put back into the head. To prevent it from rattling about, he packs the inside of the skull with *The Irish News*. So there you have it,' I concluded.

'Surely it's not normal to want to see that?' she ventured, as she reached into her broad uniform pocket for her cigarettes. She gave me one.

'It's part of the training, Sister – just part of the training.'

She then asked me if I'd mind taking down my guitar from the luggage rack and starting a sing-song, which I did. Songs popular at the time were *Blowin' in the Wind, The Universal Soldier, Colours, Mursheen Durkin, Fine Girl You Are* and *The Leaving of Liverpool*.

I had just finished the last verse of *Mr Tambourine Man* when Long Tommy leaned over me with his big, bony right hand fixed in the shape of a Colt 45. A straight, yellow, nicotine-stained finger trembled nervously only inches from Sister's left ear, as his narrowed lips made a smacking, popping sound every time his thumb moved forward. Six 'shots' were fired in rapid succession into the side of Sister's carefully groomed head and then, as if nothing had happened, he turned quietly and walked slowly back to his seat.

'When's the post-mortem?' I laughed.

'What post-mortem?' she asked, as if struggling to break away from a daydream.

'Your own,' I chuckled, before once again realising I was very much out of order and not behaving like a student nurse should. She pulled deeply on a fresh

Benson and Hedges and slowly exhaled, calmly exclaiming, 'Oh,' as if paying me no attention. She turned slowly and, doing her best to face me in such a confined space, her turf brown, searching eyes, adopted the stare of authority and her full lips prepared to move.

'Nurse Hanvey, during your training at the School of Nursing, did Mr Kinsella or Mr Crangle ever advise you how to properly address and speak to your senior nursing staff, to show them the courtesy and due respect their position deserves? Were you taught that, Nurse Hanvey?'

'I'm sorry Sister. Please forgive me. I was taught the proper procedure, but I suppose I wrongly believed that differences in rank could be relaxed just for today because of the day trip.'

'Whilst on duty or off, you are a nurse first and foremost and it would do well not to forget that fact. Remember, your ward reports, your behaviour and that includes your behaviour today, are all recorded and assessed and used when your final examinations are marked. So it is to your benefit and your benefit alone that you learn to present yourself in a more professional manner.'

She's one rotten, rank-pulling bastard, I thought.

'I'm sorry Sister. Please forgive me. It won't happen again.'

'I sincerely hope not, Nurse Hanvey.'

If only Long Tommy's gun had been real and blown her fuckin' head off.

Long Tommy hadn't a care in the world. Six feet seven in his bare feet, he was one of the few patients at Downshire who amazed me to the point of bewilderment and fear. Twenty years earlier, Tommy and some friends were packed into the front row of their local village cinema gaping wide-mouthed as 'Big John' fought it out to the bitter end with the 'Injuns'. During the final minutes of the film, as the audience clutched the edges of their seats, Tommy produced an air rifle from a meal-bag, took careful aim and fired, hitting 'The Duke' right between the eyes. The screen gave a loud crack and split in two and local officers from the Royal Ulster Constabulary removed him pronto. The local judge declared he had been 'highly irresponsible' and the local newspaper gave him the classic headline 'Local Man Shoots John Wayne'. After that, he was admitted to his local mental hospital and detained at Downshire ever since.

He loved watching cowboy films on television, but only if those same cowboys were chasing Indians. He hated movies about outlaws such as Jessie James and Billy the Kid and couldn't understand why the Lone Ranger never shot Tonto. During the gun battles on the burning plains of Texas, he'd slowly draw his imaginary six gun, which was anything but imaginary as far as he was concerned, and let it fly at the screen. He would discharge the usual half dozen rounds and then swing the barrel upright to his mouth and coolly blow away any remaining smoke with one short puff. He would reload rapidly, jump from his chair as if bitten by a million fleas, pull up the corner of the large floor mat and quickly empty the 'chamber' at what I'll never know, before returning the covering to its former position.

Long Tommy had a body scientists would die for, but it always amazed me to see how it worked. Few individuals alive have escaped the compulsion of masturbation and Tommy was no exception. So engrossed was he in these frequent exercises, he remained totally oblivious to any nursing or domestic staff who were forever walking past him in the course of their duty. He'd give the odd curse or two and continue with his business and in time the staff also became blind to his not unnatural behaviour. He always did it stark naked while sitting on the edge of his bed. Ward maids would glide past with their mops and buckets, pretending not to notice, but the part of the floor opposite to where he sat was always given more attention than the rest.

A female nurse once told me that female patients in their seventies also did it, which she said was part of their second childhood and, she maintained, was something associated with touch.

Tommy was different from anyone I'd ever seen before and he really made my skin creep. Two fully blown breasts decorated his chest like balloons on a Christmas tree and as he gained momentum with a well-practised right hand, his left continuously explored and caressed his massive mammaries. As Vesuvius erupted for the umpteenth time, they slowly became less aggressive and wobbled to steadiness again, as a Chivers jelly might do just before it sets. Then through frosted eyes of haze and glaze, he'd calmly look at me as if he had been interrupted while writing a letter. 'Oh, it's you Nurse. Make me a cup of tea.'

Long Tommy was seated in the back seat of the bus, beside Cecil the Charge Nurse. Tommy point blankly refused to sit beside any female and knowing him it was easy to understand why. He didn't have to.

It was a momentous occasion for patients who occupied a disturbed locked ward to have a day out. A few years earlier, some of the more forward looking staff, headed by the Chief Male Nurse, Jack Lees, had decided to throw open the gates and make the hospital more accessible to the community at large. Open days and visits were organised and encouraged and were quite revolutionary. More humane thinking became the norm. The efforts of this far-sighted nursing team proved most successful in breaking down the barriers associated with mental illness and Downshire became a shining example to other institutions in England or Ireland.

The hospital's former Victorian title of Down Lunatic Asylum had long since been changed to Downshire Mental Hospital. A partially successful push to have it recognised as Downshire Psychiatric Hospital never really caught on, with people in the fairly large catchment area still referring to it as the Mental. It probably made some people feel superior. The less fortunate within the walls were a useful yardstick for outsiders to measure their own standing and success in society.

The bus was now snaking its way though Belfast's narrow streets and smiling, laughing, cheering faces beamed out frantically at the 'normal' people walking here and there and going about their daily business, all of them oblivious to the happiness and sense of adventure held behind the perspex windows of that old Ulsterbus. On outings such as this, cursing by patients was almost non-existent, yet back on the wards at rising time on ordinary days the language was vile. Today, the anger, which prompted such profanity, simply wasn't there.

At intervals more frequent than usual, young nurses would zig-zag up and down the aisle of the bus, dishing out endless cigarettes to eager, hardened smokers. Chronically disturbed patients weren't allowed to carry their own cigarettes and matches were totally forbidden to them. During times like this, I would talk to Sister about my studies and forthcoming exams and basically try and pick her brain on the finer points of mental nursing.

'Sister, would you explain to me the difference between neurosis and psychosis.'

She would then proceed to tell me that the neurotic built castles in the air and that the psychotic was the fellow who moved in and lived in them. So, in many ways, it was much better being a neurotic.

'Are you studying much, Nurse Hanvey?'

'Yes, a bit Sister. Not as much as I should, but I'll

cram it in, in the weeks before the exam.'

'Sometimes cramming it in simply doesn't work. How many girlfriends have you got now?' This was a question I felt had little to do with exams and before I could answer, she advised me that too much recreation didn't fit into the pattern of success in nursing. After this statement, I realised that everything could be connected to nursing.

'Are you singing much on radio now, Nurse Hanvey?' she enquired.

'Not much. Just a little. The programme producer, Maurice Leitch, is going to England to concentrate on writing.'

'Get this unholy slut off me. That painted whore of Babylon.'

It was Big Andy. One of the female patients had sat down on his knee and put her arm around his neck. He didn't like it at all.

'Get her off me, Nurse. I wouldn't ride the bitch even if she wanted paid in Free-State money. Get her off Nurse, before I have a heart attack.' The Charge promptly removed her. Big Andy clasped his two chubby, but well-worked hands over his bulging rotund belly and once again adopted the pose of complete contentment.

Big Andy was a merchant seaman and had sailed everywhere on the face of the globe where he could find water. During the early 1950s he caught the 'clap' in Central America and had received treatment by 'hot needle'.

'Bobbie,' he emphasised, 'those black heathen bastards of doctors tried to kill me and I'd swear they were smiling when they did it. They rammed a burning hot needle up my penis and closed it over. They then pushed a button and the needle opened up inside my prick like an umbrella and they pulled it out again. The pain was unbearable.'

On my first day in Andy's ward, it was his job to take me out to the garden with the patients' work group. The Charge had appointed him to show me the ropes. Ambling down the back steps, he pointed to a patient in his early thirties. Whatever madness really was, and I wasn't so sure, I figured this had to be it - perpetual motion - not one second of stillness. With the force of a rogue elephant, he pounded up and down in an area specially sealed off just for him.

He constantly waved his arms in the air and with clapping hands and flicking fingers, he roared like a bull. He was heavily built, with the strength of steel. His laced-up, booted feet hammered the ground and the earth echoed and shook. Between roars he would chant, 'ja ja, ha ha, ga ga, ya ya, la la, ma ma, da, da'.

'Do you see him?' asked Andy seriously.

'Yes,' I quavered, thinking, how could I miss him, putting a brave face on it and hoping the wire fence held.

'Well, Nurse,' continued Andy, 'before he ended up in here, he was a bank manager, so you have to be careful in the Mental and look after your body, Bobbie. Treat it as you would a shrine and it will look after you.'

Three times daily Big Andy would announce he was going for a 'CB' which was his code for a cold bath. Three times a day, with the energy of a whale, he would splash in a tub so full, the water rolled over the edge in tidal waves and ran across the black and white, square-tiled floor. One night in winter, as all the patients and staff sat engrossed watching television, someone in the far corner of the ward let off an almighty fart.

'There she blows, Nurse,' smiled Andy, 'did you hear that prize-winner? Grab your harpoons me hearties.'

The humour now building up in the day-room was putting the TV in the shade.

'Tell him to shut up, Nurse. He's mad. I want to see the Queen on the box,' bellowed Big Davy.

'Nurse, the only time he'll see Her Majesty on that fuckin' television is on Christmas Day or nothin'. The pathetic peasant,' grated Andy.

Before Big Davy could retaliate, a second 'blast' sounded from roughly the same location.

'Did you hear that, Nurse? There it goes again. That bastard will shite himself and then we'll all be suffocated,' complained Andy.

'It's only a fart,' chuckled John Joseph, as he continued to waltz haphazardly between lines of seated patients and glide past the television at twenty second intervals, managing to annoy the entire gathering.

'No, it's not a fart, that's the Oirish love call,' quipped Andy, in a poor imitation of a Free-State accent. 'Their arses think their throats are cut. No decorum, no breeding – they're just animals. Do you see those bastards? They'd sell their arses for sixpence,' he stormed. 'Let me out of here before I choke. I'm going for a CB. Could you get me a towel, please, Nurse?'

'Sure Andy. Right now?'

'Right now. Thank you Bobbie.'

Andy gave me a call card he picked up in a Havana nightclub in the days before Castro moved in and wiped out prostitution. Printed on both sides in English and Spanish, it depicted a scantily clad beautiful Latin girl lying in the 'missionary' position. He had been there all right and he'd seen it all.

His favourite hymn, When the Roll is called up Yonder, was now being belted out by a mixed choir of some fifty mobile voices, with the big man taking the lead and conducting the lesser mortals, as he saw them, with perfect grace and poise. Sister was eating the cigarettes and matching me one for one.

'Are you still going out with Nurse Maguire?' she queried.

'Aye, indeed I am. She's coming back from holidays on Monday. I just can't wait to see her,' I eagerly replied.

'I suppose you love her?' she shot.

'I do indeed. Maggie is a good person and a great nurse,' I said defensively.

'Oh, she's a good nurse all right,' jibed Sister. 'Sing another song,' she ordered.

It was approaching ten o'clock and the early rising had at last begun to cast a temporary shadow on the now sedate proceedings. Throats and limbs were being rested and only Andy seemed anxious that the momentum should be maintained. He stood upright, his broad belly touching seats to his left and right, and ordered, 'Right, Nurse Hanvey, strike the chord of B'.

'Is that B flat, Andy?'

'There's only one B Nurse and this one's in the key of B Special,' he joked. 'Let's see if we can inject some life and drive, some good old-time religion, into this band of pitiless heathens. You all know it, for God knows I've sung it a thousand times for you. The words are 'What a friend we have in Jesus'. Did you hear that, you dozy bastards? What a friend we have in Jesus.'

Old Harry was standing behind him, carefully examining each and every word he uttered. 'Jesus, Jesus, Jesus,' he repeated, 'what a fr, fr, fr, what a, a friend... what a friend we... we have a friend... what a friend we have in, in, in... in Jes... in Jes... Jesus, in J-E-A-S-U-S. Jesus. What a friend we have in Jesus. Give us a fag Nurse.'

'Don't mind him Nurse. He's totally and permanently insane. That poor bastard is so fucked up his mother wouldn't know him. Now brethren, let's commence our little timely tribute to the Lord Jesus Christ.'

Within seconds, every voice on the bus was joining in, some in front and some behind, but all doing as best they could and thoroughly enjoying themselves. Harry was interspersing powerful pulls on his cigarette with more close analysis of Andy's words. 'What a friend we have... we have... we have a friend... a friend in Jesus. What a friend... a F-R-I-E-N-D we have. What a friend we have in Jesus. J-E-A-S-U-S.'

The Big Hotel

The big hotel looked like a hen house when compared to the sprawling chateau that was Downshire. One thing the hotel did have which the hospital did not - and it was about to present more than a few problems - was the claustrophobic, three-sectioned, revolving glass door. The boys were now all marching straight towards it and there was no way of stopping them.

'What is it?' cheered John Joseph with glee. 'It's a… it's a whirligig, it's a whirligig,' he babbled.

'Don't even bother to consider answering that Nurse. If you told the poor bastard, he wouldn't believe you anyway,' advised Big Andy.

Big Andy was jammed solid in one of the glass triangles, as tight as a tinned sardine. In the next compartment, pushing and shoving and trying in vain to get it to move were John Joseph and Big Davy. Andy's twenty stones, however, proved too much for such a delicate invention and it stubbornly refused to budge.

The hotel manager, an efficient, nervous looking man in his mid-fifties, waved frantically through the window and pointed anxiously to another door further along the building where presumably he would prefer us to make our entrance.

John Joseph, who hated enclosed spaces of any kind, was red-faced, fat and furious and was hitting the see-through partition with his fists, feet and head. His shock at being captured by such a thing probably explained his verbal silence. Andy stood erect and motionless, looking upward and praying for a miracle which hopefully would get things on the move again. Whenever trouble visited him, his ready remedy was prayer and meditation. His pattern never varied. Big Davy shouted for all he was worth and began to panic and started to punch John Joseph with short, right jabs to the small of his back. He had no room to hit him harder.

Columns of hotel staff and guests lined up on the inside, staring wildly in amazement at such an unusual commotion. On the outside, forty patients and nurses gazed across the divide into no-man's land.

His moment of prayer completed, Big Andy edged forward slightly, his massive frame grazing the circular brass wall. Feeling movement and obviously believing they were going to be catapulted into oblivion, John Joseph and Big Davy began to push frantically in the opposite direction. Thumping, banging, flailing and finally cursing, they were quickly ejected back to where they'd started from, pulling Andy out after them in the process and forcing him to keep running for a short distance in order to maintain his balance. The staff and guests on the inside applauded and we cheered.

'Well to hell with that for a contraption,' laughed Andy, 'I thought I was in there for life. The biggest whore in Havana wouldn't get me back into that kip-shop.'

'It's not funny, it's not funny,' whinged John Joseph, who was jumping towards me in anger and pointing at Big Davy.

'He hit me, Nurse, he hit me. That bastard hit me in that… that… greenhouse! I'm not going to get in there again. I'm going home, I'm going home.'

'I didn't fuckin' touch him,' insisted Big Davy, who never admitted to anything.

'Did you take your dinner, Davy?'

'What dinner?' would be his never changing reply.

By this time, the manager was approaching, carefully edging his way through the happy gathering and trying hard to give the impression he wasn't frightened, when we all knew only too well he was.'

'Can I help you, sir? I'm Mr Turner,' he said to Charge Nurse Cecil.

'Indeed you can, we're on a trip from Downshire and we're very hungry.'

Everyone in Northern Ireland had heard about Downshire, so there was no need to elaborate. John Joseph was smiling wildly and showing many stumps of well-ground teeth and making demands, 'I want Irish Stew and fried eggs and bacon and cabbage and jelly and tea too!'

Mr Turner gave Cecil a puzzled look as if to say, 'Does he really want all that, or does he know what he's talking about?'

'Yes, give him all he wants. This is his day out,' replied Cecil.

Mickey Mooney was seven feet tall and always licked his lips, even between meals. The very mention of food sent him running in the direction of the canteen. As the other patients finished their courses, Mickey would sit watching the bowl of soup, the dinner and the dessert. The minute his cup of tea was placed before him he'd shout 'bowl' and as soon as the domestic had answered his request, the soup, dinner, dessert and tea were all emptied into it and stirred up.

'Why do you eat like that?' I would ask.

'That's the way it ends up in the stomach Nurse, so why give my stomach extra work when I can do it first,' he would laugh.

It seemed to make some sense to me, but I never tried it. I was too afraid. Cecil did not dare to risk any more 'seizures' in the revolving door and the manager led the way to the other opening, some twenty yards away. On entering the plush foyer, the first person we saw, standing in the middle of a line of tourists and smiling his head off, was John Joseph.

'I did it, Nurse, I did it,' he beamed.

The tourists looked at one another and then at John Joseph and then at us.

'You did what?' Cecil asked with a knowing grin.

'I spun through the glasshouse. I did it! It worked!' He was delighted.

'Good going,' replied Cecil. 'Well done.'

John Joseph had broken away from the main party and made a second attempt. I admired his determination – especially after being so frightened the first time.

Deep, red carpet, the type which invites you to lie down on it, expanded to every corner and corridor as far as the eye could see, as two ornate but complicated chandeliers swayed ever so gently, giving off just enough light and no more. I wish Christmas would hurry up, I thought.

Bouncing Jeffrey had worked in circuses and shows all over Ireland as the Rubber Man, doubling as a rocket when he played his other role of The Human Cannonball. He had also ridden the wall of death and too many falls had probably contributed to his present condition.

With the poise and grace of a ringmaster, Jeffrey commanded the attention of the entire gathering. He stepped forward and announced in a clear, resounding voice: 'Ladies and gentleman, for your entertainment tonight, from the darkest forests of coldest Russia, flown in at tremendous expense, for tonight and one night only … I give you … for the first time in Ireland … Bouncing Jeffrey, The Rubber Man. He went quickly into his never forgotten routine, hands nimbly replaced feet, as he tumbled, cart wheeled and rolled, inches from the encircled throng, knocking the occasional cigarette from astonished lips with flashing, flying feet.

For a man of fifty plus, his act of years ago was still

intact and honed to perfection. On his final revolution, a beautifully arched, salmon-like back bowed, as he landed lightly in the upright position. Tourists and hotel staff applauded wildly as they searched each other's faces for obvious signs of approval – whether through sheer enjoyment or deadly fear, I just wasn't sure. My father always maintained, and I fully agreed with him, that applause was one of three things - faith, hope or charity.

On the strength of Jeffrey's superb performance, the patients moved speedily amongst the residents, 'tapping' them for cigarettes and absorbing whatever apparent happiness they could find.

'I want my tea now,' coaxed John Joseph.

'You're getting your dinner first, now relax,' I assured him.

'I don't want to relax, Nurse. I want my tea, I want my tea now. If I don't get my tea, I'll wreck the house.'

I knew he wouldn't and once again he soon settled down.

Robert Morgan never spoke unless spoken to, but being a compulsive reader, he had a terrific command of the English language. Fed up with the depressing sameness of his job as a fitter in the shipyard, he moved to the other side of town and opened up 'shop' - as a doctor. He had no qualifications, but having read all the relevant medical books and with a brass nameplate, carefully inscribed by a friend in the metal department, he soon enjoyed the comforts of a new and more lucrative social standing. That was 1948. Two years later, the police stumbled onto his scheme and he eventually ended up in Downshire, where he once again became known as The Doctor. Six or eight feet to my left, Robert, was busy introducing himself to an American tourist.

'Good morning, Madam, I'm Doctor Morgan, psychiatrist. Just out for the day to keep an eye on the patients and so far, so good.'

'I'm pleased to meet you, Doctor,' she smiled, through a mouthful of carefully manicured teeth. 'I'm Dorothy Silverstein and I simply adore your country. It's so beautiful... makes a pleasant change from Boston.'

'Been to any good tea parties lately,' he teased.

'If my memory serves me right, and I can't be sure, I think the last 'dish' of tea I had was in 1773,' she laughed, appreciating his knowledge of American history.

'And what's your profession Dorothy, apart from being a very fine historian,' he probed with humour.

'I'm a simple housewife, Doctor.'

'Call me Robert,' he purred.

'Thank you, Robert, that's less formal. My husband was a company director, but he died last fall and my sons insisted I came to Ireland on vacation, so here I am.'

'I'm really sorry to hear that Dorothy. I hope he didn't suffer too much in his final days.'

The crafty bastard, I thought. Here she was, falling for it, hook, line and sinker, or maybe she was desperate and had little choice.

'No, it was a massive heart attack. He never knew what hit him. Still, my two boys are carrying on the business and things are going really well,' she explained.

Realising I was within ear-shot, Robert gently putting his hand to the small of her back and deep in conversation, slowly manoeuvred her towards the bar.

'Excuse me, Doctor,' I fawned, 'may I speak to you a moment?'

Robert stepped up to me and spoke loudly, 'Yes indeed Nurse Hanvey, how may I help you?'

I discreetly lowered my voice and warned Robert not to leave the hotel.

'Oh no Nurse, I shall be available of course, should any emergency arise.'

He dismissed me with a friendly smile and wave of his hand and rejoined Dorothy, explaining that the nurses relied heavily on his expertise.

'That's another problem's solved, so how about a drink? You will allow me to buy a beautiful lady such as yourself a drink?' he charmed, obviously relieved at not being exposed.

'Oh, why not,' she revelled, 'I'll have a gin and tonic.'

'A gin and tonic for the lady and a double scotch, bartender,' he beamed. Frantically searching his inside and then his outside pockets he finally threw his hands up in amazement before hitting them off his thighs, 'Gosh Dorothy, I'm terribly sorry. I seem to have left my wallet in the car. I can't leave the hotel in case the nurses need my help. Let's see if the Charge Nurse is about. He'll help.'

'You'll do no such thing, Doctor, sorry – Robert, please allow me,' she insisted as she opened her purse and told him to help himself.

'Oh, no Dorothy, I couldn't possibly… such a trusting lady.'

'Gee Robert, if I can't trust a doctor, who can I trust?'

As she proffered the roll of bills, he delicately withdrew four crisp, brand new Ulster Bank twenty-pound notes, promising to return them later in the day. I couldn't believe my eyes, but kept on watching just the same. Within seconds, the friendly barman had set up the drinks on a highly varnished counter and Robert, having folded one of the notes in four, deftly pushed it between his first two fingers.

'Keep the change,' he winked confidently.

'Thank you very much, sir,' returned the barman, 'you're very kind.'

'Not a bit,' dismissed Robert, in a stiff, upper-crust, but most impressive accent.

'A nice chap, Gordon, he always looks after me when I visit my clinics in the area,' he spoofed.

She raised her glass to meet his and smiled warmly.

'Good health, Dorothy and coming from a doctor you'll appreciate that's very good advice indeed.'

'Robert, I believe you kissed the Blarney Stone.'

'No, Dorothy, I swallowed it,' he chuckled.

Fifteen minutes later we were in the main dining hall, surrounded by a cluster of well-tanned, happy summer faces. Robert was directly to my left and Dorothy and a group of American friends sat at the table behind us, by the large bay window overlooking the sea. During the soup, a powerful voice mimicking the Reverend Ian Paisley, boomed and stressed.

'Do youse sinners believe in the Lord Jesus Christ? Have youse committed any untold acts of fornication today? If youse have, you'd better fall on your knees in the sight of God and repent; I said repent friends, before it's too late. I don't care if you're in and out or up and out, brown and white or black and white; you can be Chinese, Japanese, Cantonese or Vietnamese. I don't care, friends, if you allegiance is to the White House, the House of Representatives or the coal house. I tell you now, you stand naked today before your Maker, cowering like fools, waiting on the death sentence to be passed. Are you prepared for the final chapter, friends, before you're delivered to the arse-burning pains of Hell? Tell me friends, are you ready?'

Two male nurses apologised to Dorothy and her friends before marching the 'Reverend Eddie' back to his dinner.

'Let me go, you Fenian rabble,' he shouted, struggling half-heartedly to break free.

'These Papists are trying to silence God's man in Ulster and if they think for one minute they're going to gag God's man and prevent him from spreading the word of the Lord Jesus Christ then I've got news for them. They might as well be trying to stop the Niagara Falls with a pitchfork.'

What an orator, I thought. He's fuckin' brilliant, but

I reminded myself that when one incident like this happens it's usually followed by another - and sure enough it was. Big Davy gathered speed as he charged across the floor to a table occupied by female patients. He crept up behind the stoutest and quickly cupped her breasts with two brawny nicotined hands.

'Yo, yo, yo, yo,' chanted Davy, with a fat smile at least half a mile wide. Alice bounced to her feet in hysterics.

'Sister O'Flynn, he grabbed my diddies. He hurt my diddies, the dirty oul' bastard.'

Big Davy was unceremoniously led back to his table, roaring at the top of his voice.

'I never touched her diddies, she's a lying bitch. Diddies, diddies, diddies! All I ever hear is diddies, diddies, diddies! What the hell do I want with diddies?' he finished, exhausted, before collapsing back into his chair.

Good answer Davy, I thought. Well done.

The female tourists were disgusted – or so it appeared at the time.

As deserts were being attacked with hefty spoons and an orchestra of hinged elbows, I casually glanced to my left, where my worst fears were realised. I had lost a patient, my first, and this was the worst fate that could possibly befall a psychiatric nurse.

I walked briskly to the next table and told the Charge that Robert was missing. In turn, he moved toward the nearest waiter.

'Excuse me, we're a patient short, did you see a man of five feet nine in a tweed jacket and spotted dickie-bow tie?'

'With light grey slacks and patent black shoes?' he replied.

'Yes, that's him, where did he go?' asked Cecil.

'He's with Mrs Silverstein. They've gone to her room,' he pointed in the direction of upstairs.

'Christ,' replied Cecil, 'take me there.'

Scanning the dining area, I soon discovered that her seat, like Robert's, was empty.

'He's riding her,' cheered John Joseph, who along with half a dozen of his comrades had now joined the posse.

'He is, my fanny,' beamed Big Andy who had told us, in the furtherance of our education, that backsides were called fannies in America. When asked what they called fannies out there, his reply was 'the same as they call them here'.

Big Cecil tore up the stairs behind the waiter. Through countless corridors of carpets we surged, until the rush stopped abruptly outside the door of room 429. The door was identical to all the others but the deafening sound of classical music beating its way through wood and mortar told us a party was in progress.

'Turn it down,' bellowed Davy, pulling his coat over his head in an effort to close out the din.

'Ah Beethoven's Ninth,' enthused Andy as he hummed along with the Berlin Philharmonic, conducting every instrument to perfection with the tip of a 2B pencil.

'I love Choppin,' echoed John Joseph, unable to get

his tongue around Chopin.

'Ignore him Nurse,' laughed Big Andy, 'the only thing that poor bastard will ever chop is sticks.'

The Charge's fist kept a steady dull, thud, thud, thud in the middle of the panel just below the numbers 429.

'He's at her,' chirped John Joseph, 'he's at her, Nurse.'

Seconds after the music ceased, a small lady, liberally sprinkled with gold and diamonds, appeared in a full-length, towelling dressing gown.

'Can I help you, sir?' she gleamed.

'I am looking for Doctor Morgan and I believe he's with you?' enquired Cecil.

'I'm here Cecil,' called Robert, 'please enter, Nurse, and bring the boys with you.'

I had never seen such luxury before. This hotel had to be six star at least - drinks cabinet, built-in wardrobes, crystal chandeliers the lot, and over in the corner at a darkened table for two, sat the bould Robert smoking a big cigar and politely sipping from a glass of Napoleon brandy. A loaded chess-board sat proudly in front of him. A stack of ten-pound notes to his right, left me in no doubt that they'd been playing for money and he was winning.

'Beautiful holiday weather, boys,' twanged Robert, as he casually blew smoke upward over a perfectly planned and extended lower lip.

Cecil grinned his legendary grin, unconsciously stretching it from ear to ear. He looked at his watch and then directed his gaze towards the corner and Robert.

'Well Doctor, time ticketh away and if we're going to

see the shops and take a dander round the town, we'd better make tracks and anyway I'd like you to have a look at John Joseph, he hasn't been feeling too well.'

'Certainly Cecil, a brilliant idea. Just wait until I put on my jacket.'

'I'm not lettin' him near me. There's nothin' wrong with me. He was at her, Nurse. Look! The bed's wrecked, he was at her. He's mad! I'm not lettin' him near me, he's sufferin' from a multitude of disarranged ideas and inflicted with a mass inferiority complex too!'

'Tut, tut, now, now, John Joseph, take it easy,' calmed the Doctor.

'Sorry, I have to go Dorothy, duty calls. I'll be in touch.' As he spoke to Dorothy, their eyes met, but his right hand, which appeared to have a mind of its own, quickly scooped the pile of notes and buried them deeply in his hip-pocket.

'He's fuckin' stole the money,' snarled Big Davy.

'I don't think a man in your position needs to take money from a lady visiting our country for the first time,' cautioned Cecil.

'Of course you're right, Nurse,' agreed Robert as he placed the money back firmly on the table.

'No, please take it,' demanded Dorothy as she crossed the floor and gave it back to him. 'You won it fair and square, please take it,' she insisted.

'No thank you Dorothy. Buy yourself a new dress on me, as a memento of an unforgettable afternoon.' He kissed her on the cheek and apologising for the interruption, Robert took her hands in his and said,

'Goodbye, lovely lady.'

Downstairs in the bar, Cecil ordered orange juice for the company. Half an hour later, as glasses were constantly being refilled and cigarettes being replaced, Big Davy staggered across the floor singing at the top of his voice. The words of *Danny Boy* had been changed to *Davy Boy* and sounded just as good, if not better, than the original. Hacking hiccups ensured Davy's lyrics overlapped those of the gathering, but the singing continued regardless and no-one seemed to notice. As every voice reached the point of delirious crescendo, a sudden, deafening silence filled the room as an empty brandy bottle, which hadn't been jammed tight enough into Davy's pocket, tipped out and clunked dangerously onto the highly polished wooden floor. Rolling even and long, like a 'brattle' of thunder, it finally stopped at the base of the bar counter with every eye in the room quietly following its progress. It was the very same bottle I'd seen in Dorothy's room a short time earlier.

'Davy, where did you get that bottle?' asked Cecil.

'What bottle? I didn't see no bottle,' he snarled.

'He stole it, he stole it off the oul' doll,' persisted John Joseph.

'I didn't 'stale' no bottle,' roared Davy, as he took one almighty swing, catching John Joseph on the point of the chin and knocking him stone cold to the floor. With his balance already gone, Davy made a few perfect revolutions before ending up on top of his comrade who was already fast asleep.

The remainder of the day was relaxed and without major incident, as we demolished ice cream and sweets and lay on the beach in eighty degrees of sheer bliss. All patients had donned broad straw hats because their main drug, Largactil, whilst being a powerful 'calmer downer', made their skin super-sensitive to the sun's rays and they would have easily fried without this protection.

After tea at eight o'clock, Cecil stood in the middle of the foyer and announced it was time to board the bus and head for home. A big cheer went up and died down again. A solitary voice hidden in the crowd quietly exclaimed, 'fuck it'. It was almost, but not quite, the end to a perfect day.

Coming Home

The evening sun struggled to make this the longest day of the year, but it found the going just that little bit too hard.

Twin rows of overhead seat lights bathed us with their sallow softness and grew brighter, only to fade again, as the engine coughed and revved in preparation for the long journey home. Behind us, an ocean of dying crimson spread across the sky like a purple vestment, as young student nurses dished out pocketful after pocketful of cigarettes to some of the most hardened smokers in Downshire. Fifty transistor radios tuned to as many different stations were pressed to the sides of happy, sleepy heads, grasping for enjoyment with their last ounces of rapidly flagging energy. Even Big Andy sat motionless, with hands clasped and eyes closed, deep in prayer. There would be little singing, if any, done tonight.

'That – that – that fucker … he stole my rock and took a bite out of it. He … he took a bit of it, Nurse,' stammered John Joseph.

'Give him back his stick of rock and settle down,' ordered Cecil, the Charge.

Cecil was the toughest nurse to work for in the entire

hospital. With him patient-care was the main priority and he made us toe the line. We dreaded being sent to his ward, but in time we grew to like him and he soon earned our respect.

'Did you enjoy your day, Nurse Hanvey?'

'Yes Sister, very much, thank you.'

'Do you not think you were a bit lax in letting Robert Morgan escape with that American woman?' she probed.

'He wasn't going anywhere. He was only enjoying himself. I can't see what all the fuss is about. Anyway, the Charge Nurse seems to think it's over and done with, so that's good enough for me.' I replied, angry and peeved at her latest onslaught.

'How dare you speak to me in that tone, Nurse Hanvey? Have you no respect for authority? It would serve you well to remember you exams are coming up soon,' she stormed.

'You do what you have to do, Sister, but I think you are being extremely unfair.'

'Nurse Hanvey, what you think counts for nothing and don't you ever forget it.'

I didn't answer. The next words spoken came an hour later when an unmerciful thump almost demolished the side of my ribcage, as her elbow dug me swift and deep.

'I see you are looking after your patients as you were taught in Training School,' she said sarcastically.

'Jesus, you scared me! I'm sorry Sister. I'm very tired and I must have dozed off. I promise it won't happen again.'

'Sleeping on the job, Nurse, sleeping on the job cannot and will not be tolerated. I will be reporting you to your Unit Officer tomorrow.'

'You can tell him tonight for all I care,' I countered, no longer willing or able to take any more of her aggression.

'Nurse Hanvey! Would you mind repeating, slowly and clearly, what you've just said to me.'

'Please forgive me Sister, I'm sorry. I had a few Bacardis back at the hotel and Bacardi always has a strange effect on me. It makes me anti-social. I'm not normally like this.'

'Ah, drinking on duty as well, Nurse Hanvey! I'm afraid this will go very much against you in your ward report and I intend to see it does.'

A good fifteen minutes passed and she never spoke a word. Most of the patients were now fast asleep and snoring their heads off. I was fighting to stay awake and I thought I was dreaming as her face drifted closer and touched my shoulder.

She was now looking at me in a way that was completely out of character for someone of her rank. She smiled as I hadn't seen her smile before and it was quite beautiful. It also disturbed me. Desperately, I tried to figure out exactly what was going on.

Beauty was a quality I'd never recognised in Sister O'Flynn. In fact, her more than generous build led some female staff to christen her with the nickname - Click of the Heels. She was tall, regimental and a stickler for discipline, but with more than a little femininity. Click of the Heels painted disturbing images of concentration camp commandants and torture, but she was widely recognised as a first class nurse. The male staff simply referred to her as Mighty Tits and I had no need to wonder why.

She gazed at me in a playful way and smiling broadly with lips closed she tucked her chin tightly against her chest and with clipped razor sharp diction said, 'and he huffed... and he puffed... and he blew the house down.' Her long fingers tickled me in the ribs as I remembered my mother doing when I was a child.

What's going on here? I asked myself. Here I was exhausted and browbeaten by this psycho and all she could do was recite nursery rhymes. The soft, deceptive glow from the yellow lighting was playing tricks with my eyes and no matter how many times I tried to focus on reality, she appeared more attractive than the minute before, leaving me in a state of wild confusion.

'I think the patients are ready for another sing-song, Nurse Hanvey. Would you mind taking down your guitar and singing for us?'

'Oh, so it's 'us' now, is it?' I mimicked. 'OK, Sister, I'll do it!'

'That's the attitude, Nurse Hanvey. I'll make a nurse of you yet,' she smiled.

During the second verse of *The Leaving of Liverpool* with every voice on the bus raised, including Cecil's, something caught my attention that caused me to gaze in disbelief. I was sure and then I wasn't, so I looked again to try and convince myself I wasn't imagining things.

Her uniform seemed to be getting shorter and was already three inches above her knees. Perhaps it happened, I told myself, when she had sat down and it had just ended up like that, or maybe it had been that way all along and I simply didn't notice. Some men can instinctively read female body language. I wasn't born with such a gift. I always had to be certain before I made a move. In fact I almost wanted it in writing.

With no space whatsoever between us, I moved even closer until the heat of her body penetrated my clothes like a bowie-knife. She was approaching boiling point. Nervously, I stroked her palm, searching for a reaction. None came. Soft smooth thighs lay moored in silence as my fingers commenced their long, slow journey. Her skin burned back at me as if in revenge, but she never flinched.

Why am I doing this? I asked myself in wonder. She had given me a terrible day and made my life a misery. It was so obvious she disliked me intensely, but there was something powerful about her that was drawing me. Maybe it was her rank or maybe I longed for an easier passage through to my final exams. Whatever it was, I didn't know. I was stumbling blindly, as though in a desert, not knowing what I was going to find.

Minutes later, my fingers had reached their destination. Their journey had ended and she appeared to be fast asleep. Jesus, I thought, what if she really is asleep and wakens up to find me doing this? I'd be accused of 'attempted interference with a sleeping ward sister', or of 'tampering with authority'. There was no greater crime in the book than meddling with the comatosed. I would surely fry. The judge would throw the book at me. In fact, I could picture him leaning on his bench in disgust and peering over his horn-rimmed glasses before sending me down for twenty years.

It didn't matter what the exact title for the crime I was presently committing was, he would have half a dozen legal terms for it. An obvious one would be 'behaviour likely to lead to a breach of the peace'. I would be sacked in disgrace from nursing and would probably be given the nickname Rob the Dead.

My finger, which had no such worries about legal terminology, was moist and trembling, keeping up a steady, even rhythm. Her knees were now lax and pliable as my hand fought for more room. Her thighs swung open like a well-oiled door and with eyelids closed tighter than a window blind, perfect teeth bit randomly, on a full bottom lip. Staff and patients were bawling *The Yellow Submarine* when her muscles tightened in racking spasm and nearly pulled my hand off, as if in the throes of an epileptic fit, causing her legs to go rigid and her feet to disappear underneath the seat in front. Her eyes glazed, hazed and disturbed, searched vainly for something, but appeared lost and out of control.

Her previous dignified composure was long gone as I maintained the momentum and kept the pressure on.

Her head moved in ratchet fashion, ever so slowly, each 'click' bringing it forward and outwards from the seat. She had arrived at the end of her 'journey', with beads of fresh sweat resting and streaking a water-laden face.

'What have you been doing to me, Nurse Hanvey? I must have been dreaming,' she sighed, settling back into the relaxed position.

Now, I'm for it, I thought.

'I couldn't help it Sister. Please forgive me,' I said hoarsely. I was about to say it wouldn't happen again, but refrained in case I annoyed her, and I definitely didn't want to do that. She took my hand in hers and squeezed it, smiled and said, 'sure, there's nothing to forgive, Bobbie. Come closer to me.'

She handed me a packet of cigarettes and asked me to light two, which I did, while my mind raced to make sense of what had happened.

As that reliable old Ulsterbus chugged its way through the avenue of trees, Downshire loomed large and eerie in the crystal moonlight. Tired patients scrambled down noisy metal steps and were counted once again. Our day trip was over.

'Sister, can… can I see you again?' I hesitated.

'Aren't you on duty tomorrow?'

'Yes, I'm not off till Friday.'

'I know that. I checked your work rota yesterday,' she said coolly.

The Arrangement

As time elapsed, Sister O'Flynn's appetite for the unusual bordered on gluttony, which I had always believed was one of the Seven Deadly Sins, among pride, covetousness, lust, anger, envy and sloth.

It was a well-known fact in nursing at the time, that if you wanted to proposition a woman you did so on a Friday afternoon when she wasn't working the weekend. It was on a Friday afternoon such as this in the nurses' canteen, that she set out to further my education.

With a cup of tea in one hand and a cigarette in the other, her main worry in this life seemed to have something to do with her age, which in itself was something I knew nothing whatsoever about.

I believed life was one long adventure and the energy I possessed at the time was something that God had given me forever. I had nursed the old and the infirm and sympathised with their condition, should they be bedridden, or just able to hobble about, and so you'd think having had such experience would have given me some insight into the future. But I still believed that infirmity, ill health and having to slow down, would never happen to me. These guys were just plain unlucky! At twenty-two, I was bouncing without pain or ache and this was the way it was always going to be as far as I was concerned. No one had told me otherwise.

'My husband doesn't love me,' said Sister O'Flynn and she went on to explain that she was forty-five and had missed out a lot in life. I knew her husband very well and had been drinking with him for a few months. Paddy was full of love. He had treated me to supper in Rea's Restaurant, brought me Green Chartreuse when I hadn't the money to buy him one back and helped me to my room in the nurse's home when I was too drunk to make it on my own. Yet, here she was running him down behind his back and trying to convince me he was a bad man, when I knew only too well he was definitely one of the best!

I didn't know it then, but in later life I was to discover that this was one of the first points in conversation used by women out for a good time. That simple line, 'my husband doesn't love me anymore,' said it all. A statement such as this was like using Gelignite to open your front door when a less dramatic entry would suffice.

'I like you very much,' interrupted my pattern of thought, as she gave one of those baby smiles that I knew to be popular in business such as this. Every time she appeared at the tea table, the top three buttons of her ward sister's uniform always remained open, revealing heavily stretched sunburned skin as far as the eye could see, which in reality wasn't far, but far enough to make me wonder where the white began.

'You make me very happy, Bobbie,' she confided.

'Thank you Sister, you're very welcome,' I answered, thinking that if my mother ever taught me anything she taught me good manners. County Fermanagh was Ireland's heartland for good manners and wasn't that where I came from? Mother would remind me constantly that 'good manners were easily carried,' to which my father would add 'aye, and they cost nothing as well!' I always remembered that.

'Nurse Hanvey, it's like this,' she said sternly, as if trying to shock me back into listening to her again. She looked at me clinically as her outstretched finger brushed the back of my hand. She said she would be asking me to do some things for her and that as I grew older I would learn to appreciate why she had asked for my help that day.

'You may or may not enjoy what is going to happen between us, but if you say yes, I will help you with your studies. I'll get you old examination papers and at the end of three years I'll ensure you are a fully qualified psychiatric nurse,' she added.

What a salesman, I thought. Jesus, she must be planning to get me to murder her husband and him one of the nicest fellas I've ever met. Look at all the cigarettes and whiskey he's given me. I'll be locked up in the Crumlin Road jail for ten lifetimes and I'll never see Maggie again.

'Nurse Hanvey, are you listening to me?' she demanded, as she inhaled deeper from her new cigarette.

'Yes, Sister, whatever you need,' I gulped.

'It's good I can count on you, Bobbie, but as yet I cannot say what it is I want you to do for me,' she smiled.

'You do know where I live, three miles out the Ballybunny road?'

'Yes, indeed I do. I know it.' I agreed, not wanting to offend authority with a smart answer.

'Well, as it happens, Nurse Hanvey, I was looking at your work rota on the notice board today and I see you're off duty on Monday next. He's working in Belfast on Monday and won't be home until four o'clock.'

Oh my good God, I thought, she had the whole thing figured out. This was definitely going to be murder with a capital M. I'd be killing Paddy around tea time, hardly giving him enough time to take his coat off, put on his slippers and sit down beside the fire to read the papers.

'I want you at my house at one o'clock,' she insisted.

Unable to take any more of the suspense and believing I had a right to know what was going to take place, I decided to take the bull by the horns and place my cards firmly on the table.

'Right, Sister, do you want me to poison him, or shoot him?' I demanded, unconsciously raising my voice just that little bit too high.

Suddenly, heads, uniforms and chairs turned and were facing in our direction from various points throughout the canteen. They gazed at us with shocked, disturbed faces that demanded an immediate explanation. I shrugged my shoulders and smiled over at them, as if I was only joking and laughed the whole thing off. Now the police would have dozens of reliable witnesses. In fact, they'd have so many, they probably wouldn't bother to call them all.

'Nurse Hanvey, what are you talking about?' she snapped, while speaking low from the corner of her mouth, like an amateur ventriloquist struck down with palsy. 'Wise up, you silly, fucking, loud-mouthed prick,' she fumed.

'Look,' she sighed, taking a short, quick pull for a Benson and Hedges, 'all I want you to do is come to my house for your dinner on Monday. Do you think you can do that much right? Anyway, don't worry, we'll have a nice time,' she laughed, as she slid the tall salt cellar across the table and into my half open hand. Her laugh bothered me.

'OK then, I'll see you on Monday.' I agreed.

Montana Moriarty

Getting up early on Monday morning, I shaved, washed, dressed and threw my dirty clothes into the communal washing machine. I went down the stairs three steps at a time and into the common room, where residents would watch television and relax.

It was completely empty and I must admit I always liked it that way, because every time I walked on its highly polished, hollow wooden floor, it echoed sharply and deeply, like fresh sods thudding on a coffin lid. This sound gave me the uncomfortable feeling of possessing more authority than I felt I was entitled to. Such were the simple pleasures of youth, when sounds and smells were appreciated and interpreted to a point well beyond my reason. Sitting down in the corner armchair, which was my favourite, I turned on the electric fire with the toe of my shoe and lifting *The Irish News,* scanned the latest happenings in the world at large, outside the safe perimeter of Downshire Mental Hospital.

When I looked out at the wall of windows in the Female Nurses' Home, only thirty yards opposite, I could see Maggie's bedroom with the curtains still closed. She had been on night duty and probably wasn't long in bed. I remember thinking about how she was and missing her terribly. She was the only one true love I had ever known, yet here I was, about to start walking in the ice and snow to visit Sister O'Flynn, whom I didn't love and she knew it, but it didn't seem to make any difference to either of us. One thing was for sure, it wasn't my heart that was making me go there. Maybe it was curiosity, or simply the anticipation of doing things I hadn't done before.

Going out through the front door of the Male Home, I bumped into Staff Nurse Moriarty from County Kerry. Because of her massive breasts, the boys had christened her Montana having heard that the mountains were huge in 'the treasure state'. A recurring joke at the time informed us that if Montana should fall on her face, she would strike oil and those who knew her said she had nipples as big as budgies' heads.

The name Montana Moriarty sure had one hell of a ring to it. Being heavily into country music, she followed Big Tom and his band the Mainliners to dances all over Ireland. She knew every song he had ever recorded and never failed to let us know when he had a new one due for release. From May till September, when windows in the Nurses' Homes were seldom if ever closed, her record player would be turned up full blast so that we too could enjoy the talents of Ireland's undisputed 'king of country music'. Songs such as *The Carroll County Accident, BJ the DJ* and *The Old Log Cabin for Sale* were played so often, I knew them better than she did. I suppose, for that at least, I would be eternally grateful.

The result of her travels following the show bands meant that she was off work more times than she attended but, being a brilliant nurse, was well thought of by the Hospital Administration. They were happy to tolerate her shortcomings. She was allowed to do her own thing and remained a very happy and efficient human being.

She was singing loudly and happily at the top of her voice a song which was popular in Ireland at the time:

'Shall I ne'er see you more, gentle mother,

in the fields where the wild flowers grow;

I am sorry for that loss I can't recover,

'neath yon willow lies my gentle mother low.'

'Good morning, Nurse Moriarty, you're one fine singer.'

'And the top of the morning to ye, Bobbie. Thank you, I can only but do my best,' she replied in her soft Irish brogue.

At that time in mental nursing, numerous girls from the Republic of Ireland came North to do their training and many of them settled in Downshire and the Downpatrick area after qualifying, only returning to their homes when they died. Few of them ever married, but instead totally devoted their lives to caring for the patients and, in sharp contrast to Ulster girls, they possessed a quality of innocence and deep, religious conviction so beautiful it had to be experienced to be believed.

'And how's the world abusing you, Montana?'

'Sure isn't it abusing everybody, not me alone,' she

laughed.

'If you happen to see Maggie, would you tell her I'll see her in the canteen, at teatime?'

'Yes, Bobbie, I'll do that, to be sure.'

The snow was falling faster now, bringing with it a silence that suited my own expectant, bewildered mood.

Within an hour, I was standing in the welcome warmth of Sister's highly decorated front room, gazing out onto a living Christmas card, if ever I'd seen one. Her long white lawn, randomly planted with tall-needled fir trees, looked very much at home in this seasonal landscape.

Red robins danced and kicked angrily on the fluffy ground. They were confused and baffled as to where all the little worms had gone and were not at all amused with the new icing on their Christmas cake. I saw their predicament and sympathised with them. Their present task was almost an impossible one. The sorrow I felt brought me back in a flash to my childhood, to the day when I found the wounded frog in our garden.

My da had said, 'Don't worry son, they eat them in France,' to which I replied gruffly, but under my breath, 'Dirty bastards.' I cried that day and when neighbours enquired of my mother as to why I was in such a distressed state, she replied, 'Ah pass no heed on him. Sure wouldn't he cry for the ducks going barefoot!' Such was the philosophy of life when I was growing up in Brookeborough in the 1950s. This was one of the earliest lessons I ever received in the art of learning to 'paddle my own canoe' and I must admit, it was a good one.

The only signs of human habitation out front were my footprints, which began at the base of the heavy mahogany gates and stopped dead at Sister's front door step. The snow was coming heavier now and my tracks were being filled in right before my eyes. There I was, warmly and safely inside her home, without even a trace of my arrival and I remember thinking it was like pure magic. Now you see it, now you don't.

Ever since the time I spent in England, singing in dingy folk clubs and sleeping rough in various accommodation, from miners' security huts to Salvation Army hostels, I appreciated warm rooms and especially those looking out on cold settings such as this. I never wanted to be cold again.

As I stood there in Sister O'Flynn's living room, I noticed that for some time, the kitchen where she was preparing dinner, had gone deadly quiet. I wondered if she was loading the gun for the final showdown, or adding paraquat to the Coca-Cola. Just as I had finished thinking that, a strained voice, full of authoritative command, gushed in my direction.

'Nurse Hanvey, come here immediately.'

Now I'm for it. It's me she's going to shoot! I thought. I stood rooted in shock and felt the blood draining from my face like a burst hot water bottle. Outside, snowflakes still putted and melted on the warm windowpanes.

'Nurse Hanvey, come right here, when you are

fucking called,' she shouted.

I noticed how she never failed to add the 'g's' to her word endings, but I still couldn't be convinced that it sounded any better than fuckin' without the 'g'. During my school days in County Fermanagh, my mates would laugh me to ridicule and call me a sissy if I ever used a 'g', so for many years afterwards, I fell into line and never used one at all. They would say it was only Protestants who spoke like that and the last thing they wanted was to be mistaken for a Protestant. It was a problem to start using them later on in life. Sometimes you managed to get it right and sometimes you didn't. I turned out of the living room and stepped into the hallway, stopping abruptly in the darkened kitchen doorway.

Standing with her back to a roaring Aga, wearing only her nurse's uniform which hung open from neck to knees, Sister O'Flynn, revealed heavy breasts and a full, round, soft belly. Black nylons and matching suspender belt completed the effect, with carelessly painted blood-red lips and darkened-down eyes thrown in for good measure.

The air was thick with the smell of boiling cabbage and raw whiskey. Three tins of bully-beef were stacked precariously on the cooker's shelf. In her hands she held an expensive cut-glass sugar bowl. And there was I, expecting her to be wielding a double-barrelled shotgun!

Later in life, I would learn to understand and even curiously appreciate such behaviour, but at twenty-two years old and having just arrived from the 'bogs' of Fermanagh, I looked upon all this theatrical stuff as nothing but a short-cut to the fanny. There was no tugging at skirts or pulling of elastic here, no quickness of the hand to deceive the eye. This was definitely the open door.

'Nurse Hanvey, remove your trousers right now,' she commanded.

I thought her order was anything other than friendly and rather than 'remove' them, I took them off slowly. Carefully resting the sugar bowl on the table in ritual fashion, she lifted a milk bottle from the midst of discarded cabbage leaves, grabbed me by the willie and doused it all over until no part remained untouched. Soon, anxious, flicking fingers were scattering pinches of sparkling white sugar crystals all over the fresh sticky fluid. She knelt down quickly on the brown oil-cloth, which was specked with more of the crackling granules and indicated with a straight, falling finger that I was to kneel also.

'Kneel, Hanvey,' she pointed, now dropping the title of nurse. The boys in the Nurse's Home often maintained that when women go over forty they like to bark and meow when sexually aroused. I prayed she wouldn't ask me to become involved in this stuff because I was very religious and not a cat or dog – I would remind her of this if I had to. Anyway, I got the clear feeling she didn't like me very much. She held out reaching, tacky fingers and, taking my hands, began to recite a prayer. Being a good Catholic from birth, I automatically joined in without being asked to do so and without thinking why I was doing it.

'Nurse Hanvey, we are all corrupt and depraved in this life,' she preached. 'We are filled with evil, filled with lust and filled with sin.'

'And filled with shite as well, Sister.' I interjected.

She went down on all fours and began licking the milky, sugary mess.

So much for hygiene and the proper nursing procedure, I thought. She was trying to catch it in her mouth, with no hands, again bringing me back to the Halloweens of childhood when I'd bob for apples in George Kirk's scullery. Sometimes you caught one, sometimes not. Her mouth was quickly filling up, with some stuff sliding from its sugary corners and a look of pure madness in her rolling cataleptic eyes - that beautiful cemented stare of temporary insanity. Before I had time to save myself, she pushed me backwards onto the floor, kissing me hard and at the same time releasing everything she'd taken from me back into my mouth.

'Drink this, take it back you fuckin' bastard, drink it!' she ordered, in a mumbled scream, as she tried to smother me with caked, gooey lips. She had just dropped her very first 'g' and exposed her true station for the first time.

When it was over, she stood as erect as a ward sister should, rubbed her lips dry with the back of her hand, dusted her uniform with sticky, flicking fingers and turned her back on me, slowly trying to restore her previous composure of respectability.

'How are your studies coming along, Bobbie?'

'I'm doing the heart and lungs at the moment.'

'Mmm, heart and lungs, very interesting subjects indeed. I'll get you some good papers on those tomorrow. Are you still seeing Maguire?'

'Yes, I am, every day. She's on night duty and I'm having tea with her shortly.'

'Stay here for your tea and I'll tell him you called in to borrow some books. Go to the bathroom and freshen up and I'll tidy up down here,' she insisted, as she pushed me along the hall, and directed me towards the landing. After brushing my teeth and washing the sugar down the sink I was close to vomiting and repeatedly asked myself why I'd done this. The sin I'd just committed had to be high on the scale of the mortal variety and the fact that one of the 'biggest' prayers in the Catholic religion had been desecrated in such an irreverent way would only compound my crime in the eyes of God.

This was not me. Yet, I had gone along with her and if pushed on the question, I would have to admit I enjoyed the experience, but only at the time and definitely not now. I was feeling all the guilt in the world - the exact amount of guilt that my religion expected me to feel. Surely, no amount of genuine prayer would get me out of this one. If I told the priest in confession, I doubt if he'd believe me, so I decided to adopt the safe approach and say nothing at all. There was no point in me disturbing a decent man like Father Burns, who would never think the same of me again.

Tiptoeing downstairs, I quietly turned the lock and gently closed the front door behind me. Three months was long enough and I just couldn't take any more.

Running out into the snow, she begged me to stay, as frozen flakes melted and streaked on her still naked breasts, now goose-pimpled and angry with cold. I kept on walking, telling myself over and over again not to look back. When the snow melted, even my footprints would be gone.

The Canteen

The canteen clock showed five when I joined Maggie at the corner table. A pile of nursing books stood neatly stacked beside her left hand.

'Hi, Hanvey and how was your day?' she enquired softly.

No one else ever called me Hanvey and no one ever made it sound so good.

'Oh, I'm just back from Sister O'Flynn's house. She gave me some old psychiatry books. She said she didn't need them anymore.'

I felt the room close in on me and wanted to end this conversation as quickly as possible. This was known as the lie nearest the truth - the one that's always told.

'I don't have to tell you what I think of O'Flynn. After all, she did try and split us up but it's best to let bygones be bygones. In spite of our rows, I still admire her very much. She's a great nurse.'

Maggie had been my constant reminder of all that was good in life. For the first time, I began to feel awkward and ill at ease in her company. The almost visible unreality I was experiencing invaded me like a surgeon's knife. It was as if my body wasn't my own anymore. Looking through the window at the naked, blue sky, I prayed for clouds and rain. I wanted someone to reach down my throat and pull my insides out.

'Hanvey, you seem lost. Is it something I've done?'

'No Maggie you haven't done a thing, I'm just tired after walking in the snow.'

'I know how you feel. I almost fell coming up the steps from the home. They say it's going to lie for another two days. That's all we need. I hate it when the thaw comes.'

'I hate it too. I'm sorry for being in such bad form.'

'You're hopeless, do you know that? Come on, give me your hand.'

As she squeezed my fingers, I saw her eyes clearer than I'd ever seen them before. They were moist and lovely as if touched by the morning dew.

'Maggie.'

'Yes, Hanvey.'

'Hello sad eyes, what's up?'

'It's my old neighbour from home, Michael Cody. You'll remember me talking about him. When we were small he used to scare us to death with all his ghost stories. He was eighty last week. Well, my mother phoned this morning and told me they buried him yesterday.'

'I'm sorry to hear that Maggie, I know you were very fond of him.'

'Indeed I was, a great old character from a different world than ours. Did you know he could dance and play the fiddle at the same time? All he lived for was his hens. The neighbours were never short of eggs. He saw to that and no longer ago than Sunday last he walked the three miles to Mass. If he doesn't go to heaven, then there's little hope for the rest of us. Hanvey, would you do something for me?'

'You've only to ask.'

'Would you drink a cup of tea with me in memory of old Michael?'

'Of course I will,' I answered, but I felt I hadn't even the right to use her name.

In the process of adding sugar to my tea, as she'd always done, my finger touched the spoon and stopped it inches from the cup.

'No thanks Maggie, I don't want sugar.'

'But you always take sugar you big eejit.'

'Not anymore, I've given it up.'

'But it's not Lent yet,' she giggled in disbelief.

'I know. I decided to give it up. I don't want it anymore.'

With two cups raised, we touched them together and echoed, 'to Michael'.

I never took sugar after that and she never asked me why.

The Big Dance

Every event of social importance organised at Downshire was always held within the lofty confines of the Great Hall. Unlike the remainder of the hospital, with its miles upon miles of drab, grey paint and endless whirlpool of churning, cranking locks, this hub of prayer and recreation pointed the way to change in what had previously been called, or more often whispered, the Lunatic Asylum. It was a welcome patch of sand in the middle of Alaska.

The weeks leading up to Christmas and the New Year were wonderful times to be nursing in Downshire and the most looked forward to event of the year, the Patients' Annual Dance, was with us once again.

In the cold winter of 1967, something arrived unexpectedly in Northern Ireland, something that was to put a major damper on the season's activities. Anthrax, one of most feared diseases in the farming community, ensured that all visits to the hospital were cancelled until further notice.

It had just turned seven thirty on the night of the dance and various wards had already begun to empty their human cargoes into this theatre of mirth and enjoyment.

A country and western band, booked for the occasion, was told to stay at home as were the local branch of the St Vincent de Paul who did tremendous charity work in each and every one of the thirty wards. They would bring presents, provide entertainment and take time to talk to the old folk who'd never been spoken to. Incidentally, there was no ward 13, but 31, for whatever reason, always raised the temperature of superstition in this most pseudo of religious atmospheres.

The blue, square record player sitting on the stage floor belted out the hits of the day via a big silver microphone that rested on a small cushion beside its loudspeaker. After poaching the cream of talent from patients and staff, the Chief Recreation Officer, Colm Campbell, arranged an 'emergency' programme and promised us the greatest show on earth.

Big Andy and the patients from the 'deeply disturbed' ward, where I was presently placed, were on a constant quest for cigarettes and their 'mooch' had already begun. They were canvassing the hall like clergymen at a garden fete.

I watched with interest as Fidelma O'Drenalin, a staff nurse from the refractory ward, briskly climbed the side steps to the stage, with long, strong, determined limbs and quickly disappeared behind the curtain, followed by half a dozen of her 'understudies'. Fidelma never realised her true profession in life. Although in her mid-thirties, she still longed for the day when a talent scout from Covent Garden would show up at one of her performances and whisk her away to a new career in opera.

Possessing a unique talent, her perseverance with the patients bordered on the saintly. At eighteen stone, she was built for comfort and not for speed and her massive lungs never failed to swell the front of her black sequinned evening dress. The boys always waited for the high notes. Once, on a roasting hot summer's morning, she passed through the occupational therapy department where Big Andy was heard to quip, 'If she fell on her face she'd strike oil'.

She had worked on her 'understudies' over a number of years and it was quite uncanny to observe these souls, who found it difficult to tell the difference between time, place and person, singing opera at the drop of a hand. Fidelma's husband, Benny, had left her five years earlier, not because he didn't love her anymore but because their home was small and the constant high-pitched singing almost drove him mad. After this, she moved out of Downpatrick and became a permanent resident in the Female Home.

'Oh blast him', she would say in a fair attempt at an 'upper crust' English accent. 'When I have tea with Callas, he'll sit up and listen. Then and only then, will the poor wretch regret scorning my talent'.

Maggie breezed into the Great Hall from the 'female end' with Staff Nurse Smyth and twenty or so patients, who immediately melted into the rapidly expanding crowd. Seeing her walk over reminded me of our first meeting in Finneston House.

'Hi Hanvey, I hear there's no band. It'll be a hoot tonight,' she exclaimed, with raised eyes and an infectious impish smile. 'It appears all visits are cancelled and we're to survive in total isolation, but what can we do?'

'Aye, it's Anthrax and the authorities don't want it to spread.'

'It's foot and mouth Hanvey, so you'd better watch out. You'll never guess what happened to me today,' she enthused.

Already knowing her answer, I quietly waited for her reply.

'Sister O'Flynn took me into her office, sat me down and made tea. She apologised for sending me to Matron and said she'd sort it out and, wait until you hear this, she hoped we'd be very happy together and thought we were well matched. I always told you Sister was one of the best.'

'And you believe her?'

'Why shouldn't I?'

Realising I'd asked the wrong question, I added, 'I'm really pleased things have worked out well for you.'

My lips touched her ear.

'I love you very much Maggie.'

'I love your too, you Fermanagh bogman and I'd do anything for you, except that one thing which will have to wait until we're…'

'Yes, until we're married,' we rhymed in unison and laughed happily as we'd always done.

'Maggie, I want to taste your breath.'

'In here! In front of all these people! You must be daft. Later!'

'I've been to England but I've never been to Galway. Will you tell me all about it?'

'Yes, if you like. It's beautiful, but the best way of knowing is seeing and don't forget you're asked to our house in the summertime, just in case you have made any other plans.'

'I wish it was summertime now.'

'Don't worry, it won't be long.'

As she was lighting two cigarettes, I accidentally glanced over her shoulder. Sister O'Flynn was approaching fast and in order to warn Maggie I smiled broadly and raised my voice louder than was necessary.

'Hello Sister O'Flynn and what takes you to the opera?'

Quickly dropping the cigarettes, Maggie automatically straightened her nurses' cap, even though it was perfectly positioned, and turned around.

'I'm very sorry Sister, I…'

'Nurse Maguire, is this the way you observe your patients? You've left Nurse Smyth on her own.'

'I asked her permission to come over here. She's covering for me. The two doors are manned so no one can escape.'

'Don't you dare speak to me in that tone of voice. Your Free-State manners are not quite up to Northern scratch. Remember, whether on duty or off, the patients are your responsibility and if one goes missing then your job's on the line.'

'Fuckin' bicycle,' I mumbled, unable to take any more of her bullying, which was aimed at Maggie but also directed at me. There followed a quick eyeball to eyeball with Maggie, a sharp click of the heels and she rotated and faced me. Her complexion reminded me of the old bus conductor who used to ferry us daily to the Tech in Enniskillen. We had christened him Cherry Blossom after the shoe polish.

'Nurse Maguire, did, did, did you hear what this, this bastard's after calling me.'

'I'm afraid I didn't Sister,' she smiled and made a bad situation worse.

'He called me an 'effin' bicycle and we all know what that particular piece of Fermanagh rubbish means. Have you, have you ever … Nurse Maguire do you know what is meant by the term bicycle?'

'It's a means of transport, Sister, with two spoked wheels, one in front of the other. The rider sits on a saddle and the whole contraption is driven by two pedals.'

Keeping a straight face wasn't easy and when Maggie could finally keep it up no longer, she burst into uncontrollable laughter, which she tried to stem with her hands.

Sister was livid.

'Nurse Hanvey! Tomorrow, prepare yourself to visit Mr Lees, the Chief Male Nurse. I'll be talking with him first thing. You know you really are quite pathetic, arriving here from the bogs of Fermanagh with a guitar and a few songs and no qualifications whatsoever and, by the way, your musical ability leaves a lot to be desired. Don't you agree Nurse Maguire?'

Maggie was getting fidgety and angrier by the minute and it was beginning to show.

'I have no interest in guitars or songs. That's not why I like Nurse Hanvey.'

'Why are you sending me to Mr Lees?' I asked, trying to change the subject.

'You called me a bicycle. You have no respect for authority and a gentle clipping of the wings, I think, is somewhat overdue,' she demonstrated, moving the first two fingers of her right hand towards her face in scissored fashion.

'Well, I'd like to make it clear, I did not call you a bicycle.'

'Oh yes you did and don't think you can deny it,' she blustered, baring her teeth in the process. 'If you're thinking of taking me for a fool, then we'll not be long seeing about that.'

'If you'd like to know, Sister, I called you an icicle because of the cold way you treated Nurse Maguire and in addition you broke the rules of nursing protocol by chastising her in front of me.'

'Oh now we're being very smart, Nurse Hanvey, far too smart for your boots.'

She was stunned by the turn of events, as Fidelma's voice raised the roof and had John Joseph darting through the crowd with his hands to his ears trying to escape from the opera. Whilst he found most of Fidelma's repertoire bearable, *Caro Nome* from *Rigoletto* drove him berserk and a few nurses had to restrain him for the five or six minutes it lasted. Some yards away on my left, he was on the floor waiting for the last glorious note, which would once again release him from his 'captors'.

I figured that if I kept my face straight, I could convince Mr Lees I said icicle and Sister had already figured the same.

'Nurse Hanvey,' she thundered, 'if you think this little episode's over, then you're living in dreamland. Let's just wait and see shall we? God is always on the side of those who wait.'

With another solid click of the heels, she instructed Maggie to resume her duties, spun quickly around and pushed her way through the crowd that now filled the hall to capacity.

Big Andy, who was standing beside me, beamed a 'beamer'.

'I think she likes you Nurse Hanvey. I went to bed with one like her out in the back streets of Havana before that beardy bastard Castro shipped them out. In my book, Sister is definitely the business. Thank God I'm celibate or I'd take her round the back of the boiler house. Look out Nurse, she's coming back.'

'Jesus! Now I'm for it.'

'Nurse Hanvey! Come here, I'd like a word with you.'

'Excuse me Andy. Yes, what is it Sister?'

'You bastard! How dare you make little of me in front

of my junior staff? And by the way Nurse, does your darling Free-Stater know about the wee mole high up on the inside of your thigh?'

My heart sank. I saw she was deadly serious.

'Nurse Maguire and I don't have sex and we're not having any until we're married.'

'Well, law de daw,' she mocked. 'Am I listening to love letters from the Vatican? Do you remember that English girl you went with last summer? Surely you must know the one of whom I speak. Oh, come, come, Nurse. The International Voluntary Student, the IVS, what did we call her, Cynthia something or other? The one they all said had the Duke of Edinburgh tattooed on her tit.'

'Sister, please keep your voice down. People will hear you.'

'Now we're getting worried Nurse and with good reason. Well, I'll be telling your sweet virgin Maggie about your mole. I think you were deeply in love with her around the time you were downing darling Cynthia. Isn't that right, Nurse Hanvey?'

'Please don't tell, Sister. I'm sorry for being cheeky and for calling you a bicycle, I'm truly sorry.'

'Now you're learning Nurse. It can be a painful process but if you use your thinking mechanism it doesn't have to be. Enjoy the remainder of the evening and I'll see you tomorrow and remember, before you step into bed tonight, kneel down and beg God's forgiveness. You'll find our God is all embracing and all forgiving. He hates the sin, but He loves the sinner.'

'Goodnight Sister.'

Andy was behind me. In fact, he'd been behind me all of the time.

'Nurse Hanvey.'

'Yes Andy, what is it?'

'Had the English girl - please tell me Nurse - had the English girl His Royal Highness tattooed on her breast?'

'Yes Andy, His Royal Highness on her right and Ghandi on her left.'

'My good Christ Nurse, that's ridiculous'.

'Well, there you have it Andy. It's a strange old world.'

'You can say that again, Nurse. You can say that again.'

Fidelma was taking her final bow and probably thinking of Milan when Colm strode across the stage and placed his left hand on the microphone.

'Ladies and gentleman, let's have one more big round of applause for our beautiful friend from the heart of the refractory ward - Downshire's answer to Maria Callas and, if I might say so, light years ahead of the prima donna. We are truly fortunate to be able to witness such an unselfish talent... a talent so accomplished, she has made Verdi, Bellini, Rossini and all the great composers, household names within the walls of this hospital.'

The staff and patients stood facing the stage with eyes agog in wonder. They hadn't a clue as to what he was talking about.

'Ladies and gentlemen, let's show our solidarity, our deep felt gratitude... put your hands together for the

Diva of Downshire ... Staff Nurse ... Fidelma O'Drenalin.'

The broad flash of her perfect 'operatic' teeth said more than a thousand words and the hall erupted with thunderous applause.

'And now,' continued Colm, 'let's put our hands together for her backing group, the Arias.'

Heavy boots thumped the sparkling pine floor and the Christmas streamers and decorations, some of which supported 'ANTHRAX DANGER VISITORS KEEP OUT' signs, swayed gently throughout the full length of the hall. The rumble persisted as Colm tapped the microphone and called for order.

A solitary voice from the front row cried out in protest. It was John Joseph.

'Fuck the opera, Colm Campbell. Put her out and keep her out. I need a tablet Nurse. My head's sore.'

At this point, Fidelma blushed her biggest blush ever and led her understudies off centre stage.

Colm Campbell was a lovely man and a good one too. Originally from the County Tyrone, he was yet another of the many staff who had travelled over a hundred miles to obtain work and settle in a strange community where the 'outsider' was forever referred to as the 'blow in'.

As Chief of Recreation, along with Ian McKenzie, an affable Scotsman who was Head of Entertainment, his efforts were revolutionary at the time and the envy of every mental hospital in Ireland and England. Benefits derived by the patients were astronomical - a visible sign that things in this old institution were changing and would never be quite the same again.

'Ladies and gentlemen,' boomed Colm, 'it now falls upon my shoulders to render an old ballad and, thanks to the wonders of modern technology, I'll be singing this one along with the greatest Irish folk group the world has ever seen - the Clancy Brothers and Tommy Makem. Nurse Breen, please be kind enough to start the record player.'

Nurse Breen scurried from the side of the stage, carefully dropped the album on to the turntable, selected the track and flicked the start mechanism. Sinking both hands deep into smart trouser pockets, Colm threw his head back and waited for the music to start.

'Come single belle and beau unto me pay attention
Don't ever fall in love 'tis the devil's own invention
For once I fell in love with a maiden so bewitchin'
Miss Henry Attabell out of Captain Kelly's kitchen
With my toor a loor a li and my toor a loor a laddie
With my toor a loor a li and my toor a loor a laddie.'

As they might say in the movies, 'the joint was jumpin'. Everyone was dancing and joining in the chorus. The place had erupted. Some were jiving, others jigging and a few were even waltzing to this most energetic of songs. The enjoyment was hectic and it couldn't get much better than this. So much for the Anthrax.

Big Andy was not amused. With arms folded, his bloodshot eyes rolled skywards in plain and utter disgust.

'Let's stand back, take a deep breath and look at them Nurse,' he cautioned in all seriousness. 'Let's both of us savour the moment and learn from the ways of sin. Behold those bromide belles of Babylon steering those poor bastards with their hoppin' diddies and gingham frocks into the dark, dripping hedges of hell. Thank the Lord, I've seen the error of my ways and am no longer tempted by the steaming flesh of a heated concubine. Praise the Lord! Look at all those distorted faces Nurse, blank sheets of paper never again to see the print of day. All on automatic-pilot, nurse, being spun into the realms of relative oblivion by this so called Irish diddleedee ... tunes inspired by the black bogs of mayhem and murder and hatched on the crossroads to hell ... lyrics written in moonlight under the spell of the poteen-still and ether cabinet ... the devil's music, foreign to the ears and mouths of all good, God-fearing, Ulster Protestant folk. I know you're a Fenian nurse, through no fault of your own and, if you don't mind, I'll close my eyes for a few seconds and block out all this decadence and say a few quiet words of praise to the Lord Jesus Christ.'

Folding two massive hands, he brought them to rest on the top of the biggest, roundest belly in Downshire and with head bowed and eyes tightly closed, his lips began moving in silent prayer.

'Andy, that was absolutely brilliant, easily your best sermon to date. You are a wonderful orator.'

Jabbing me in the ribs with a giant elbow, his lazy eyes opened slowly and a fledgling smile crept across his face and exploded into half toothless laughter, which he tried to camouflage with a lowered upper lip.

'Thank you very much, Nurse Hanvey, for your kind assessment. Now, like a good Christian, would you for fuck's sake shut up and pass me one of those cigarettes.'

'I'd say that homily was a prizewinner and worth at least five Park Drives. The hospital buys them and we smoke them, so here, put these in your pocket.'

As Colm fired himself into another verse of *Courtin' in the Kitchen,* I noticed the Moocher Muldoon tiptoe stealthily across the stage directly behind him and stand looking down in amazement at the square, blue gramophone. Gesturing with turned up palms he was shouting at it for all he was worth. The Moocher's profile was legendary. A long hooked nose, with permanent 'built on' drip and sunken cheeks, enhanced by years of sucking on damp cork tips, made him resemble a new moon.

Purple, tastefully lit, back drapes threw him into solid silhouette, as he fumbled at contrary trouser buttons. With the power of a garden hose, he let fly right into the middle of the square, blue record player.

'Jesus! Did you see that Andy?'

'That poor bastard's permanently fucked up and suffering from creeping dementia. If you wired him to the grid at Ballylumford power station for electric therapy, it wouldn't make him any wiser. He's the saddest case ever I've come across'.

An almighty bang shot across the hall, as cracks and sizzling invaded the public address system and magnified the event in full stereo. The dancers spun to a halt in disbelief. Like the true professional he was, Colm sang on regardless, now unaccompanied. His music had died and was belching smoke. Nurse Breen ran over with a fire extinguisher and rapidly restored normality.

The Moocher, in a state of shock and very lucky to be alive, was catapulted towards the front of the stage, knocking Colm and his microphone for six, as he cleared the crib and floral arrangements and shot eight feet into the crowd and onto the hard floor. The burnt out cork tip was still in his lips.

Quickly surrounded by a gaggle of white coats, he was brought to his feet and led back to the locked ward.

Big Andy was in hysterics, coughing and spluttering and, as usual, breathless.

'Help Nurse, help… please help me to sit down before I take a heart attack.'

His face was puce with choking laughter and much blood to the head.

'Ah! That's better, much better, thanks Nurse'.

Colm sprang to his feet, repositioned the microphone and called for some hush.

Thank God for Anthrax, I thought. What a night.

'Ladies and gentlemen,' smiled Colm, 'I'm sorry that my backing track has been put out. It appears the Clancy Brothers and Tommy Makem have been replaced with Handel's *Water Music.*'

The entire gathering roared and applauded, whether they understood the joke or not. This was the Christmas dance to end all Christmas dances and one that would be remembered by all of those lucky enough to have witnessed the great event.

'And now for your continuing entertainment,' announced Colm. 'Give a warm Downshire welcome to five very talented lads from the locked ward, who need no introduction to those of us who love and appreciate all that's best in the world of Irish traditional music. They're not known as the Green Coats ... they're not even known as the Red Coats, but to you they're no strangers... put your hands together and raise the roof for the White Coats Ceili Band as they give us a beautiful waltz. So, grab your partners for *The Old Bog Road*.'

Five male nurses dressed in the customary knee-length white coats appeared, took their seats, and with a couple of taps on the drum, the music began.

I scanned the revellers to check if I could see Sister O'Flynn. I checked again but she was nowhere to be seen. Staff Nurse Smyth was guarding the door and Maggie was seated to her left with legs crossed at the ankles and apparently deep in thought. I went over and joined her.

'Is O'Flynn gone?' I asked.

'Yes, she's away home. She must be cracking up because she apologised to me again.'

'Did she now?' I replied, knowing that this was possibly a good sign and to my advantage. 'Great news

Maggie. Let's go out for a smoke and celebrate.'

'Nurse Smyth? I'm going out for a few minutes, will you cover for me?'

'You don't have to ask Maggie, I'll give you a shout if I need you'.

In the main entrance area, off the Great Hall, we turned left and climbed half a dozen or so steps of the long staircase leading to the psychiatrists' private rooms and offices and sat down.

'Did you smell the whiskey on her?' said Maggie. 'It almost turned my stomach. I felt like being sick. Did you smell it?'

'No, I didn't. My sense of smell is not the best, probably too much smoking.'

'She was maggotin'. I don't know how she manages to get away with it.'

'It's very simple how she gets away with it.'

'What do you mean?'

'You know as well as I know, this place is run by the Catholic Nurses Guild, isn't that right?'

'So they say.'

'Are you a member of it?'

'No, I'm not,' she replied.

'Well, neither am I, but she's high up in the top level of the organisation. Didn't they send her to Rome during the summer? She goes on her holidays to Knock - can you imagine anyone going down there for a fortnight? What I'm trying to tell you is this. If you're in it, you can get away with murder and if you're not, you might as well be a Protestant.'

'I still won't join it, they give me the creeps.'

'So now you see why they can do as they like and throw their weight about. Do you know when we go to Mass every Sunday in the Great Hall and we kneel on the hard floor, members of the Guild kneel at the front, only they kneel on soft red cushions and pray louder than the rest of us.'

'It doesn't appear to make them any happier,' Maggie quipped. 'If that's what it does to them, we're well out of it. When she apologised to me, there were tears in her eyes.'

'Hello, wet eyes, can I kiss them dry for you?'

'Do you know, you should have been called Hanky instead of Hanvey, but would you tell me something?'

'If I can.'

'I'm worried. Please tell me what's going on between you and Sister O'Flynn?'

'Nothing's going on, what do you mean?'

My answer told her - Give me time to think of an answer - but she never noticed, or if she did she never said so.

'I saw her whispering to you.'

'With the noise of the opera and all that stuff I couldn't hear her. I told her she shouldn't have reprimanded you in front of me.'

'What did she say?'

'She told me not to be cheeky and to mind my own business or she'd report me to the Chief Male Nurse. I told her she could do as she pleased.'

'Oh well, never mind, Hanvey. Give me a kiss.'

Tell Me About Galway

The White Coats Ceili band was in overdrive. The echo of six hundred boots hammering the dance floor invaded and made the very stairs we were sitting on tremble. Overheated accordions and taut banjos competed for prominence as they discharged a reel.

Some older patients, who were allowed and trusted to wander out into the reception area, walked up and down talking to themselves but never to each other, all the time totally oblivious to our presence above them on the stairs.

Their cigarettes, forever moving up and down between chattering lips, were seldom allowed to go out.

'Maggie, how about another smoke before we go back in.'

'OK, why not?'

'I'd like you to tell me about Galway.'

'What do you want to know?'

'All you can remember.'

'Well, if you want to know, our house is on Cushla Bay right on the edge of the Atlantic. Right on the edge of the world. It's just a plain, two storey, stone house, nothing grand but solid enough to keep out the elements. The beach is really beautiful and almost reaches our front garden. Anytime there's a high wind, which is often, the sand blows underneath the door and piles up in the hallway. My mother just lets it lie there until the weather turns - there's no point in fighting with it. Some evenings after school, I remember pacing out the distance from the garden gate to the edge of the in-tide and it always ended up at ninety-seven steps. It never varied … and not having done it for years, I decided to give it one more try before I left home for nursing and what do you think?'

'What?'

'Eighty-four paces. It came down to eighty-four. I even tested it twice to make sure.'

'What happened?'

'Very simple really. My stride was longer.'

'That makes sense.'

'When I look through my front window, I can see the biggest island of the Arans, Innismore and on some days it appears even closer than on others. Some days you'd swear it was trying to get into the room beside you, even though it's ten miles away. The people who live out there, almost two thousand of them, are extremely superstitious and they make all the young boys up to the age of seven wear skirts.'

'You're joking.'

'No, I'm not. Their parents believe the fairies will steal the young boys so they dress them in skirts to help ward off evil.'

'And does it?'

'I don't believe in that stuff, but if they want to believe

that's fair enough. Who can say who is right and who is wrong?'

'Jesus!'

'Language, Hanvey. In summer it's God's own country all right, the most beautiful place on earth, but strangely enough it's on the stormiest nights in winter that I like it best. When I'm lying all wrapped up in the blankets, I love to hear the big breakers crashing away out on the bar - cracking like a rifle shot - and then to wait for the echo, as it goes right down to the bottom and comes back up again, like muffled thunder.'

'Jesus! Maggie, I'd love to lie in bed with you and listen to the sea.'

'There you go again Hanvey, taking the Lord's name in vain. Anyway you know we have to wait until we're married.'

'Yes, but could we not lie on top of the blankets with all our clothes on and listen? That way we'd be safe enough.'

'You can try telling that to my mother. She still talks about Queen Victoria. They'll never tame the Atlantic. When it's angry it can throw spray right up to my bedroom window. Some nights I love to get up and sit looking at it coming straight at me. At other times the silence is so eerie it makes you believe it's only resting before going mad again. Sometimes the silence is even harder to handle.'

I watched her more closely than I'd ever done before. The constant hint of a little tear about to overflow and tumble down her face was perhaps the most singular feature that made her so special. Gentle fingers fidgeted with the small matchbox, turning it over and over again.

'The sea's a pagan place, even more pagan than Ireland used to be and I suspect still is under the surface. The old ones used to say that on a calm night you could see the lights of America and hear the laughter of all those young Irish boys enjoying themselves in New York, but you know what my eyesight's like and my hearing's little better.'

She looked at me with knowing eyes, as much as to say, 'Now you don't mean to tell me you believe all this?'

'And then there's the big red sun slipping down into the sea - did you ever see that?'

'Never.'

'Well, at our house you can watch it all summer long. You should see the islands resting in the mist and Timothy Joyce's fleet bobbing up and down like corks on the horizon and all the time that big fireball hanging like a huge halo behind them Well Hanvey, will you buy it?'

I was still imagining the fishing boats and the pictures she'd painted.

'I've only ever seen the sun go down behind hills and houses. I'd never thought of the sea like that before.'

'That's perfectly understandable. Up in Fermanagh it probably sinks into the bogs. That's why you don't see it very often. Now tell me, will you buy it?'

'Buy what?'

'Cushla Bay, County Galway, on the edge of the world, next stop America.'

'Like the song says *How can you buy Killarney?*'

'I've little or no time for songs.'

'You want to know something Maggie, you never talk much but when you do, it's beautiful. I could listen to you all day, even if you said nothing.'

'That's very nice. You mightn't believe this, but some nights in the Nurses' Home, when I waken up at two or three o'clock, I can hear those breakers crashing and pounding away out on the bar. Then when I realise where I am, I feel very disappointed and sad.'

'Let me hold you Maguire. Sometimes when I wake up in the middle of the night I imagine I'm still an altar boy.'

'Hanvey, I'm sure you were some altar boy! Kiss me,' she whispered.

'Do you see the next time we go down to the hay shed Maggie?'

'Yes.'

'Well, you know when we're holding each other – will you tell me about Galway all over again and then I can close my eyes and pretend I'm there with you before we go to sleep?'

'If you like. You're mad y'know, but I must be as mad as you are to be telling you all these things. All right, I'll do it.'

'Do it! Now, you're talking.'

'Aye, I'll tell you about Galway, you bogman,' she laughed, 'and don't be getting any ideas.'

'You're only a Galway 'Galloot', but I love you so very much.'

'And the same goes for me, Hanvey.'

'Will we head back in now, Maggie?'

'I suppose we'd better, before they send out the search party. Do you promise to keep me the last dance?'

Two Minus Zero Part One

As I studied the notice board outside the canteen checking my work rota, she appeared beside me.

'Oh, hello Sister, I'm just checking my …'

'You're off next Monday.'

'I know, I …'

'So am I. There's a good Elvis film on in Belfast. Would you like to go and see it, all expenses paid? I'm paying.'

She was smiling and standing too close for comfort in such a public place. Staff coming and going to and from the canteen spoke to me and I wondered if anyone knew what had happened on the bus.

'I don't like Elvis.'

'But you like me and they say I look like him, well I've been told, y'know, if there was such a thing as the female version of Elvis, well then you're looking at it.'

'Yes, I suppose there's some truth in that.'

'Thanks.'

'What for?'

'For confirming other people's thoughts, y'see while other people pay me lots of beautiful compliments, you shower me with nothing but abuse.'

'Is that so? I thought it was the other way around.'

'How was work on the early shift?' she sidetracked.

'Tough, hard going. The geriatric ward's not easy.'

'I forgot to tell you my husband's cracking up. I think he needs psychiatric help. Can I see you in the canteen tomorrow at five, for tea? I'd like to talk to you about it. He's driving me up the walls.'

'I'm seeing Maggie at five for tea.'

'Don't tell me you're still seeing 'that'?' she raged.

'Yes I am. We enjoy each other's company.'

'I have no time at all for Free-Staters - who do they think they are, coming up north and taking our jobs?'

'She's not taking our jobs Sister.'

'You know very well what I mean - other people's jobs.'

'To hell with other people, they're not worrying about us.'

'That's a very selfish attitude for a nurse, Nurse Hanvey. You lack basic Christianity. You don't show love and compassion for your fellow man and remember I'm a ward sister and you are a student. You'll have to learn to show some respect.'

'Oh!'

'I'll tell you what. If you sit on in the canteen after she leaves, I'll come over and join you. I need to talk to you.'

'I can't do that, I'm walking her back to the ward. Anyway, I couldn't, it wouldn't be fair.'

'Well, we'll see what you can and cannot do, Nurse Hanvey. You'll find out sooner than you think. You're like a drunk dog.'

'A drunk dog!'

'Yes Nurse, a drunk dog.'

'I don't drink, Sister, and neither do dogs.'

'Oh yes they do. Believe me they do, and do you know how they do it? By accident Nurse… the same way as you started nursing… no education, no breeding and no manners. You're a fatal accident, but don't worry, I'll teach you to know your place. How would you like six months on night duty? Six months in Finneston House with a shovel? My best friend does the rota and believe me, I can arrange it.'

'See if I care.'

'Or maybe the Free-Stater would like six months on nights in Female Finneston. That would soon drain the colour out of those rosy cheeks. We all need sunlight Nurse Hanvey. Surely they taught you that in the school of nursing?'

'Why are you doing this to me Sister?'

'Because I like you, Nurse Hanvey, God help me I don't know why. Don't worry, I'll be in touch. I must go back to the ward and see how your sweet Nurse Maguire's doing!'

Never being content with anyone getting one over on me, I called after her, 'Fuck Elvis' and I felt a little better. She never looked around but kept on walking, with head erect and keys jangling. It was two thirty and I was totally exhausted. I opened the door to my room in the nurse's home, threw my clothes over the chair and climbed under the counterpane.

The patter of hurried, short footsteps filled the

upstairs corridor and suddenly halted outside my room door. The clock said seven pm.

'Hanvey, you're wanted on the phone. Hurry up!'

'I'm up! I'm up! Who wants me? Who is it?'

'Who do you think it is? It's Maguire. Hurry up, I want to use the phone.'

'OK, I'm up, I'm up.'

I wasn't.

Throwing my legs over the edge of the bed, my feet hit the warm floor and I was reasonably dressed in thirty seconds flat.

'Hello Maggie, what's up?'

'Hi Hanvey. Things are not good. O'Flynn's one mean, nasty bitch. She sent me to matron for not locking the medicine cupboard even though I locked the drugs' room door behind me. I'm fit to be tied, Old Lizzie Thompson went beserk and attacked the junior nurse, Nurse Jones. She cut half the face off her with a shell ashtray. You know one of those you find at the seashore and I had to go and help. There was blood all over the place. There was even blood all over my uniform when I got to Matron's office. I was saturated in the stuff. The ashtray missed her jugular vein by a hair's breadth. It was horrible and she was such a beautiful young girl. She'll never be the same.'

'Are you all right, Maggie?'

'I'm fine, thanks for asking.'

'That's all right, what did Matron say?'

'She was very nice and said it was totally out of character for me and told me to be more careful in future. She said I won't lose marks in my exams because of it and won't be marked down, so that was OK.'

'Well, that's good.'

'I've worked in Sister O'Flynn's ward many times and we always got on like a house on fire, but today, for whatever reason, well, she turned on me completely. She even objected because I was smoking in the dayroom and you know everybody smokes in the dayroom.'

'I know that. I think we should go for a walk Maggie. Fresh air is good for the soul. What do you say?'

'I'll meet you at the front door in half an hour. I'm still in my uniform. I'll take a quick bath and see you then.'

'Don't forget to wrap up well. It's freezing out there. They say it's minus two.'

'Do they now,' she laughed, 'sure when the two of us go out, that'll bring it back to zero.'

'That's pretty good, Maguire. Not bad for a Free-Stater, do you want to know something?'

'Tell me?'

'I love my wee Free-Stater more than life itself.'

'And you're not so bad yourself. I'd better rush before someone commandeers the bathroom. See you in half an hour.'

Walking the eight or nine steps from the phone box, I turned right into the long dayroom and fell back into a chair that was facing in the opposite direction to the television.'

'For fuck's sake, close the door before we all freeze,'

roared The Lid, without even bothering to look around.

Biting my bottom lip as I always did when looking uncertainty in the face, I tried to figure out a way of making O'Flynn pay for all her dirty work. My situation was the classic Catch 22, with no room for manoeuvre. I'd have to confront her and lay this ghost to rest.

From early childhood, I'd loved the frosty weather because it was the only time when I found it possible to measure my breath. With cosy hands resting snugly in long, overcoat pockets, I headed out into the whiteness. The old coat had seen better days and was approaching its sixth birthday but for some inexplicable reason those pockets were as warm as a Prime Minister's, causing me to believe I probably owned the best garment in Downshire, although I knew it simply wasn't true.

I heard the doors of the Female Home slap closed behind her.

'Hanvey, are you waiting for me or not?' she called.

'And who else would I be waiting for?' I replied, with the slightest tinge of guilt.

Up on the road, at the top of the nine steps, the tall streetlight fought its way through the fog and bathed us in its ambience. Holding her was easy. She was the only person I ever felt totally comfortable holding. My family were not 'holders', so perhaps that was where I got it from.

The weather forecast was spot-on this time. I watched

my breath disappear over her shoulder and felt the warmth of her face against mine. My eyes slowly climbed to the window above the door of the nurses' home, where a lonely, solitary figure caught my gaze. The lace curtains fluttered and fell and became steady again. It was my good friend, Sister O'Mara. She was keeping an eye on me. Soon it would be summer and she'd do it all over again - fresh salad, wheaten bread and piping hot tea ready and waiting in her flat at five thirty every evening.

Sister O'Mara's kindness was extreme but my relationship with Maggie annoyed her with a vengeance. Every time she arranged the flowers on that little dining table where we would sit together, she always emphasised this point. It was as if arranging the flowers, which were perfectly placed to begin with, gave her the additional courage to try and reconstruct my life.

I'll never forget that 15th August, the summer before. It was the feast of the Immaculate Conception. Her flat was shining the shine of redecoration as lazy air wafted through the open windows, pushing the scent of freshly cut flowers into every corner of the room.

Her deep love of flowers whittled away some of the burden of self imposed loneliness, and it made a good talking point with other members of staff who passed her door, none of whom seemed inclined to bother with her. Still, I suppose, a friendly voice for even a few minutes could remain with you throughout your day. Sometimes, that is all it takes.

'Bobbie, were you ever lonely?' She asked.

'I don't think so, Kate. It's something I never really thought about. Maybe, the closest I've ever come to it was when I lived in England, but even then it wasn't much to worry about.'

'At the speed you're travelling young Hanvey, I can see you crashing into the sun. I can safely predict that your later years, like mine are now, will be drenched with the pain of loneliness. It will gnaw at your very soul.'

I hadn't a clue as to what she was talking about, but I kept on eating the lettuce and ham and asked her why she was lonely. She had been a stunner in her time and was still very beautiful, although somewhat matronly on her confident days when she breezed about full of the joys of spring and smiled more than usual. She came from the south of Ireland and possessed those strong features - the sort I'd learned to associate with that part of the country.

Taking a carnation from the floral arrangement, her fingers caressed the fine petals and stroked them. She plucked petal after petal, as if to punctuate her conversation.

'I've never told anyone what I'm going to tell you and I've kept it bottled up inside me for thirty long years. In 1937, I was twenty. I can now see you're counting, so to save you the bother I'm fifty – not the best stage in life for a woman. Anyway, a lot of the local men had left for Spain the previous year to fight with General O'Duffy. Others went and joined the International Brigade.'

'That would have been the Spanish Civil War?'

'Yes, indeed it was. There wasn't enough fighting left for them in Ireland, so they went into the export business. Well, I knew this fella back at home in Clonavee, near Kilmichael in West Cork. He had a small farm and no interest in war. My parents taught in the local primary school and could see no one good enough for me, only a teacher you know, someone as 'good' as themselves, bright and well educated – a pillar of parochial society. Another good local lad, trained for life to stay put in the parish, to live and die in Clonavee. Holy Mother of God protect us. My life was in ruins. So Kevin sold his farm and we planned to immigrate to America.

'When the day came for us to go, my mother and a few of her friends from the Legion of Mary locked me in my bedroom and I never saw New York. They even sat on me for hours until they were satisfied his 'plane was well off the ground. Mother said it was all for my own good and I'd thank her when I got older. Kevin wrote every week, sometimes twice a week, for over two years and then I never heard from him again. I couldn't put up with the village after that – you know, the looks and the gossip from the neighbours. In the post office they'd say, 'Is there any word from poor Kevin lately. They say he's married now,' or else, 'You missed a fine one there, O'Mara'. So, I came north to Downshire. It's funny when you think of it – imagine coming to a mental hospital to get away from them!'

'What ever became of him?'

'Ten years ago they brought him home to Clonavee and I went down to the funeral. He was the first boy I ever loved and the last and you remind me of him in so many different ways. You're a bit young to understand, but talking to you brings me much closer to him. Can you appreciate that?'

'I think so.'

'So it's small wonder they call O'Mara, 'the ould maid'.'

'I'm really sorry to hear that, Kate. How did he die?'

'I was speaking to a friend of his at the funeral and he said Kevin never got over me not going with him. He lost the will to live and died of a broken heart.'

'That's terrible.'

'I don't want you to get the wrong idea when I ask you this, but it's thirty long years since anyone held me. Sometimes, I wish even a stranger would come along and hold me until they've taken every ounce of my breath away. Bobbie, will you stand up and hold me?'

'Yes, Kate, I will.'

Her arms, strong and hungry, locked themselves around my waist, making me feel secure in a distant kind of way. I held her as tight as I hoped she wanted to be held, kissed her cheek softly and whispered her name, at the same time hoping I hadn't gone too far.

We must have stayed like that for ten long minutes and when she moved away, the tears flooded down her face in a deluge.

'The last time I cried like this Bobbie was on this day August 15th, 1937. I tried to cry many times since but it just never happened. Now, be a good young fella and make us both two fresh cups of tea and I'll go and clean up this face. I'm sure it's an awful mess.'

'Anytime you feel like holding me Kate, I'll always be there and you don't have to ask, ever again.'

She walked towards me in an awkward, almost girlish way and kissed my cheek and said, 'Bless you, Bobbie, bless you'.

A short time later she returned, all freshened up, and joined me at the table.

'Kate, what became of your parents?'

'My father died in sixty-four and my mother nine months later.'

'Did you remain friends with them?'

'Once I left home I never saw them again.'

'Did you go to their funerals?'

I watched as tired, disappointed eyes filled to the brim. The carnation was bare now and the stem lay flat on the table, surrounded by the little scattered petals. It reminded me of a grave.

'No, I didn't go to their funerals. I couldn't find the love or inclination in my heart to have anything more to do with them. They ruined my life. So there you have it – you're the only one who knows my story. I hope you'll keep it close to your heart, Bobbie.'

'I will Kate.'

H anvey! Wake up, you're sleeping on your feet again.'

'God, I'm sorry Maggie, I must have been day-dreaming.'

'Well in case you haven't noticed, it's dark now. Daytime was earlier. Thinking about Kate again, were you?'

'That's true. Indeed I was, how did you know that?'

'You were quieter than usual. I know you better than you think.'

'Kate's very lonely. I saw her looking out at us.'

'She's not a bad soul. If they were all like Kate, the world would be a better place. You must be the only one who ever bothers with her, but I think that's good. She likes you. She said so. She must be one of the few people who sings your praises.'

'Aye, we're good friends.'

'You're only saying that because she makes you big meals in the summertime,' she teased, 'but don't worry, it shows a good side to you Hanvey and I like that.'

'She resents us going out together.'

'That's all right. It's only one of the problems of getting old – can I tell you something?'

'You can tell me anything.'

'When I sit my Finals, I'm leaving here. I'm going to England to do my General Nursing and then I'm off to America.'

'Now, you remind me of an Irish political party. They decided to hold a protest march from Belfast to Downpatrick, a distance of twenty miles... you're supposed to say, what happened?'

'OK, what happened?'

'They called it off in Cork.'

'Heh, heh, very good.'

'Maggie, it seems to me you're going round the world for a short-cut, but no matter where you go I'll be with you.'

'Let me kiss you for that. Hold me.'

Underneath the tall trees we held each other with the grip of death and, for the first time in my life, I felt another person's pain and realised I was the one who'd put it there.

'I hate working in this place,' she whispered.

'There's no need to do anything hasty. Sure you've still two years to do before you sit your finals. A lot can change in that time.'

'It's O'Flynn. She's really getting to me and I can't take any more of her cruel games. I used to bounce out of bed in the mornings and couldn't get onto the wards quickly enough. Now, I could sleep all day. It's even beginning to effect my studies.'

'Jesus! I've got it! I know what I'll do, I'll wreck her husband's car and slash his tyres.'

'You'll what?' she shouted. 'Who the hell have I been going out with? My God! You're starting to sound like a stranger.'

I'd never heard her lose her temper before and it stunned me.

'You will not touch his car! And anyway what purpose would that serve?'

'It would put them at each other's throats because she drives it as well. Can you imagine her face when Paddy gives her the sad tidings? There'd be some clicking of the heels then.'

'Oh, I can imagine it all right. You're not thinking very straight are you – did you not stop to consider what she'd do then? She'd carry her aggression into work and I'd have hell to pay. Please don't do it - say you won't.'

'I see what you mean. I never thought of that. OK, I won't do it. Perhaps it wasn't such a good idea after all.'

As we came into the Sugar Bowl, Big Andy was thumping out hymns on the piano and leading both staff and patients in full voice.

'Let's welcome my good friend Nurse Hanvey and his special friend Nurse Maguire to our little party of praise to the Lord Jesus Christ. Put your hands together and show some brotherly love.'

Maggie blushed and said 'Grab two seats over there and I'll get the tea' and handing me her black woollen gloves, she added, 'Here, please mind these'.

The warmth of her gloves against my face and the

smell of their freshness tempted me to keep them. For some reason, they reminded me of my childhood, which had been a happy, never ending adventure, but one that was also tinged with the many hues of self-imposed sadness. I had always invited sadness into my life as if it were my best friend. It was as if it belonged to me and I couldn't exist without it. People say this is an Irish 'thing'.

'Here Hanvey, this will warm your heart on such a cold night.'

'Thanks Maggie, your gloves. You'd better have them back.'

'I was watching you trying to eat them. Did you not get your dinner today?'

'I was not eating them, I was kissing them.'

'I know, I know. That was very special. I'm sorry if I'm a little under the weather tonight, but I cannot understand what's up. O'Flynn was always friendly. I just can't figure out what I've done to her.'

'She's drinking heavily, right? The tutor told me that alcoholics hate drink but they hate life more. Why don't you report her to Matron?'

'That would only make her worse and then what would happen when I'd move to other wards – her friends would begin where she left off.'

'Don't worry. Things have a habit of sorting themselves out. Put her out of your mind. Do you remember the night we first met in Finneston House.'

'How could I ever forget, it took me two weeks to pluck up the courage to meet you face to face,' she smiled.

'It's good to see that big Galway smile back again on my favourite face and if you'd really like to know, I was twice as nervous as you were. I couldn't believe anyone would want to make my acquaintance and from that moment you've never left my mind.'

Her hand touched mine and stayed there long enough to let me know we were as close as we'd always been.

'Go on, give me a cigarette Nurse,' demanded John Joseph, as he careered into the side of our table causing the tea to rock in the cups but miraculously not spilling a drop.

'Go on, Nurse Maguire, give me one or I'll shite myself. I'm telling you I will.'

John Joseph was speaking so fast, it looked as if he was trying to clear his mind before dropping dead. Maggie did her best not to smile and gave him an Embassy filter tip.

'Go on Nurse Hanvey, give me a light … thanks Nurse. Charge Nurse Cecil's sending me to see the Pope – he lives up in Rome in the 'Catican'. The Pope's a good Catholic, Nurse – he can hear his own confession and he smokes cigars. He's the head of the Fenians, Nurse. The priest says I'm a good Catholic. I never miss Mass. The Pope takes Largactil, Nurse, two hundred milligrams three times a day – that's why he's wise, Nurse. I'm wise too, I take my medicine. The Pope doesn't shave when he's depressed, Nurse. He's got a long beard, Nurse, when we can't see him. He wears an Aran sweater. Charge Nurse Cecil told me. Your bum's a plum, Nurse. He lives in the asylum and prays all day. He eats sponge and custard, Nurse. The Pope takes his medicine, Nurse. I take my medicine. Charge Nurse Cecil says I'm good. I'm forty next week, Nurse.'

The piano's tinkle ceased in violent discord as the eighteen stone mass of Big Andy tore clumsily across the canteen, dodging between and around tables with the agility of a rogue elephant.

John Joseph froze in terror beside my chair as Andy shook a short fat finger inches from his nose.

'Nurse Hanvey, what the hell's this heretic 'pope-in' about? That red-socked ruler of Babylon, that pale faced anti-Christ, that nicker of brass money and wooden shoes.'

When Andy verbally attacked someone, he did it through me in much the same way as one does when speaking 'through' the judge in court. This way it didn't appear like an onslaught at all and I always felt it was most clever - psychology at its very best.

John Joseph hadn't a clue what Andy was ranting on about, as he stood motionless with his right leg wrapped around his left and the cigarette trembling between his lips.

'Let me tell you something friends,' said Andy, as he surveyed the entire gathering from left to right with closed eyes and nodding his head up and down in the way the clergy often do - some call it the deep portrayal of wisdom.

'You'll have to learn to fear the Lord, you putrid purveyors of rotting flesh, you cyclothymic conjurers of idolatry, you hopeless heathens, all gathered together here tonight, in the midst of this teeming lecherous, endemic 'bowl of sugar'.

'Ooooooooh,' urged the crowd in dumbfounded admiration.

Andy grinned madly and proudly savoured the moment, but soon regained his preacher's composure and quietly continued.

'If you want to find the true Lord, friends, not the master of Mesopotamia so poorly defended here tonight by our beloved brother John Joseph, you'll have to do much better than this.'

John Joseph smiled and clapped his hands.

'Poor John Joseph hasn't a fucking clue where he is, where he is going or where he came from. He wouldn't recognise the Pope if he fell through the ceiling at this very moment.'

John Joseph looked up.

'If you want to find the Lord Jesus Christ, you've got to be drenched in the blood of the Lord, not in the sweet-smelling perfume of deception and sin. Perfume is used to deceive friends. It is used to camouflage and it is used to throw us off the scent of the Lord Jesus Christ. This way, old Satan has you firmly by the nose and leading you in the direction of despair and destruction. The choice is yours and yours alone. You've got to be paid up, prayed up, fired up and full of the word and do you see you John Joseph, you helpless Fenian – fuck off.'

Riotous applause erupted as John Joseph scurried to

the corner table and safety beside Charge Nurse Cecil and Andy returned to the piano.

Maggie winked at me and nodded with mouth open wide with silent laughter.

'And what do you think of that performance Maggie? They don't make speeches like that in the Free State.'

'I must admit he's a very good speaker. The missionaries used to go on like that when they came to our parish every winter. People used to look forward to their arrival with much excitement It was like waiting for a circus. They had us scared silly for weeks.'

'That's right. They came to Brookeborough as well. My mother thought they were brilliant and always bought me new rosary beads at the mission. They scared the hell out me, but it was fun being scared then.'

'That's true, but it can come back at you in other ways later on in life.'

'As the man says, Maggie, we'll just have to wait and see.'

'What else can we do – but right now, I think we should face the frost and go for a walk.'

'I'm sick of religion, all brands of it. I think it should be banned.'

'Now, now Hanvey, don't get cynical. It's self-destructive. Why swim against the current when you can walk on the river-bank and simply observe.'

As she lit a cigarette, I purposely watched her eyes, which were still moist and uncertain and I kissed them dry.

'I wrote to my Mum and Dad yesterday and told them you were coming down in the summertime.'

'I can't wait to see the Atlantic. Did you tell them about us?'

'Ages ago. They're looking forward to meeting you. You'll love my Dad's boat – he'll take us out to the Aran Islands. It is a place in the past, in the present, if you see what I mean. It breeds contentment. There are three islands, Innismore, Innisman and Inniseer. The first university in Ireland was built there and three thousand enrolled from all over Europe. Oliver Cromwell came along and knocked it down.'

'Maybe their entrance fees were too high!'

'No, Oliver had a serious habit of knocking things down,' she smiled.

'Well, I can't wait to go there. I can get my holidays changed to coincide with yours and then you can show me all your old hiding places.'

Her arm encircled my waist and a tired head fell on my shoulder and edged its way under my chin.

'Maguire, did you know that Oliver Cromwell only cried once in his entire lifetime?'

'And when was that?'

'When the fish-bone stuck in his throat. Would you like to play a game?'

'I'm tired, but OK what is it?' she asked drowsily.

'It's called 'know me better'. All you have to do is ask me things I like best about you and then it's my turn.'

'OK, Hanvey, here goes. What do you like best about

me?'

'The way you stand on the ground. It reminds me of the first time we met and when I look at your shoes and the laces all done up in neat little bows, I think they're the classiest shoes in the world. Now it's your turn.'

'Right, I like your gentleness and the way you treat me with respect and of course the way you hold me. You're no oil painting but I love looking at you.'

'I suppose you could say I'm more of a watercolour, but the thing I like best about you is invisible.'

'Invisible?'

'I could listen to your beautiful Galway accent forever. It has a controlled wildness about it that you never hear in this part of the country. The last words I ever hear must come from your lips.'

'A kiss for that Hanvey... and do you know what I'd say?'

'What?'

'So long, it's been good to know you... and I must be drifting along.'

'Maggie, that was absolutely brilliant. I never knew you could sing. Sing some more for me, go on.'

'Not now, maybe again. You know what I think of singing. I didn't mean what I just said,' she giggled. 'My last words would be – let me see – Yes! I have it! Good riddance to bad rubbish!'

'Maguire that's done it, now I'm going to tickle you to death and when you say stop I won't.'

My hands moved quickly, as she fell backwards into the hay and my fingers rippled her slender waist and other sensitive areas where I knew I had permission to touch. She began giggling uncontrollably and put up a hopeless attempt at trying to escape.

'Please, P-L-E-A-S-E stop Hanvey, P-L-E-A-S-E.'

'No chance – you asked for it and guess what – here it comes again, you're too late being sorry, the harm's already done, tickle, tickle, tickle!'

'Please, please stop, I'm going to… to… ahhh!'

All of a sudden she bounced upright, rolled me over and sat straddle-legged above my waist.

'Now, let's see how you like having a little of your own medicine you big bully.'

'Aaahhh! No Maggie, I'm sorry. Don't! Please don't, not under my arms – no – I can't – ha, ha, ha, ha, ha, aaahhh – Jesus don't!'

'Language, Hanvey. Now, how do you like your tickle, tickle, tickle – what's it like being on the receiving end?'

'I, I, I promise never to tickle, to tickle, aahh, don't … to tickle you again, please stop, Maggie, that's enough, we're even now.'

'You swear to promise.'

'Yes, I swear.'

'Come on, no playing with words, you swear to promise.'

'OK, I swear to promise. I need a smoke. Let me light up, please.'

'A kiss first, you big eejit.'

'Maggie, your breath tastes like wild flowers. Will you be my oxygen cylinder? Tickle, tickle, tickle.'

'Ah ha, ha, st, st, stop – please stop, Hanvey.'

Clenching her teeth tightly together, she gave a long hiss and laughed, wide-eyed and devilish as she pushed her face down close to mine and back again.'

'Hanvey! Quick, quick! The air's escaping – hisssss– kiss me before I'm breathless.'

Pulling deeper on my cigarette, I filled my mouth and our lips fused. The smoke rolled backwards and forwards and we fought to keep it there, but eventually racing pulses pounded to quietness again.

I felt the side of my face glow where it rested and listened to the steady tick of the silver watch pinned to her pullover beating in time to her heartbeat.

The frost crept in at times and touched us as we became more drowsy and wrapped in each other's arms, we entered a world of calm and silence.

Welcome to Croke Park

The next morning, Friday, was my day off. Lifting the inside phone, I took a deep breath and dialled three numbers.

'Hello, Ward 38, Nurse Smyth speaking.'

'Could I speak to Sister O'Flynn, please?'

'Who shall I say's calling?'

'It's personal.'

'Hold the line.'

'Sister O'Flynn here.'

'Nurse Hanvey.'

'Who! Wait until I close this office door… what do you want? You should know never to call me at work. Are you mad in the head or something? Still – it's nice to hear your voice. How's the studying coming along?'

'I believe you gave Maggie a hard time yesterday and I'm ringing to tell you to lay off and let her be. It's not a bit fair.'

'Are you finished?' she fumed. 'How dare you threaten me you impertinent bastard. Have you any idea who you're speaking to? I don't believe you have. Let me tell you this. When your high and mighty Free-Stater comes on duty at two, I'll be having a friendly wee word in her ear with regard to the kind of company she's keeping.'

'But, have you not already done that Sister?'

'Mark my words, I haven't even started yet.'

'Please don't, it's not her fault, and anyway she doesn't deserve this kind of … '

'What are you doing tonight?' she interrupted.

'I'm seeing Maggie as usual.'

'Oh! It's as usual now, is it?'

'Yes, it is.'

'And at what time are you seeing her?'

'After she finishes work, half ten.'

'I expect to see you down on the farm at ten-fifteen sharp. Be on time and don't be late or I'll come to the Home and get you.'

Before I could answer, she cleared her throat politely, in the way women sometimes do, and slammed down the phone.

Throughout my lifetime, it had always rained on my bad days. I told Maggie that Billy had asked me to go with him to a snooker match in Carrickfergus and postponed our rendezvous. She hoped we'd have an enjoyable evening and said she'd be in touch tomorrow.

The potholes in the farmyard were many and overflowing and trying to walk through there on a night such as this was like crossing a minefield. The wind, which had obviously gone mad, roared around every corner of that old hay shed with such velocity that it rattled my bones.

I stood in the doorway, contemplating what I might say to her and lit a cigarette. My clothes, fully changed half an hour earlier, were clumpy and sodden and rapidly becoming a separate entity. I couldn't have cared less. Behind me, in the half darkness, the sudden scuff of a leather boot against tightly packed hay almost caused the blood in my veins to run backwards.

'Christ! You scared me. Could you not have said something?'

'Sorry,' came the faint reply.

Jesus. That can't be her, I thought. Never having seen Sister O'Flynn in civvies before, it was difficult to fathom the transformation. She looked much smaller and less intimidating in that long, black coat. It was as if a different person was standing before me.

'Thanks for coming out to see me Nurse Hanvey. I'm sorry about my behaviour on the phone. As you know, I don't like being disturbed at work and anyway somebody might tell Paddy about us.'

'What's there to tell Sister?'

'I'll answer that tomorrow. Kiss me.'

'Now?'

Her lips felt totally different from Maggie's and, for a few seconds, they tasted older. An initial coldness soon disappeared as her tongue rifled my mouth with brisk familiarity.

Strong, stray fingers clawed the back of my jacket and trawled every inch of my hair and face, causing me to imagine as to how Columbus must have felt when he discovered America.

The three big brass buttons on her overcoat almost opened themselves. My hands, expecting to slide underneath a warm Shetland pullover, hit cold flesh, the shock of which almost caused me to pull back and 'sway on the ropes'. She was as naked as the day she was born, except, that is, for the long coat and matching black boots.

'Nurse Hanvey.'

'Sister, I want to talk to you.'

'And I want you to make love to me,' she clucked in an accent packed with monotone. 'That's what you wanted, isn't it?'

Her voice was getting slower, lower and more determined.

'I thought the reason we came here was to sort out our problems in relation to Maggie.'

'You know what you did to me on the bus coming back from the day trip, when I was sleeping? Don't you remember, or have you conveniently forgotten? Never start something you're not prepared to finish. It was you who started all this, remember, and don't you forget it!'

She was right. It was as if the cold clay of death was being shovelled over me and I hadn't the will to resist it.

Down in the bales, she was moving fast and speaking words I'd never heard before – words which were definitely not a part of the English language. Maybe, the explanation was quite simple and she was an Irish speaker, but having listened to Radio Eireann from childhood, I knew instinctively that it couldn't be. Anyway, Irish sounded much better than this, and whatever she was speaking she was at it hell for leather.

As well as going over all this foreign stuff, she was screeching like bad brakes and whining like a banshee. It was little wonder Paddy slept in another room.

It was hard to believe this was the same Sister of the clicking heels, who patrolled her ward in an immaculate blue uniform with starched collar and cuffs and lectured new students on the ethics of nursing. Or the same Sister, who purposely arrived late for Mass and sauntered up the aisle as if it were a country lane in summertime, showing off her latest 'gear', while the young lads elbowed each other and the ould boys knelt like greyhounds at a racetrack, ready for the off.

'Do you think I look like the female Elvis?' she would sometimes ask. 'A lot of people have told me I do.'

'Well, you've definitely got his hair and lips and I suppose the nose is similar,' I would reply.

'But, but, what about the eyes?' she would add with much anticipation, flashing the whites to make it more convincing.

'Well, yes, from what I remember of Elvis's eyes, I'd say there's definitely a strong resemblance, but can you sing?'

The reply, 'What the hell do you want for nothing?' told me this question was not part of the package.

Right now, Elvis was the furthest thing from her mind. This was beginning to look like the long haul. At times like this, I always called on outside help.

Six months earlier, also in Downshire, I became involved with a staff nurse who was known in the hospital as the Neuro and my encounter with her was still, by far, my most embarrassing ever. On that occasion, I was scolded most severely for rushing and finishing long before she did. She likened it to me getting up from the table having finished my desert before she'd started her soup.

Deciding I'd have to do something about this shortcoming, I asked some of the boys in the Male Home how they overcame this seemingly common drawback. Questions such as: 'How do you make it last? How do you drag it out?' were eagerly tackled with barrack-room enthusiasm.

'Mind over matter,' boasted the Lid. 'You need to be able to think of two things at the same time.'

Magowan maintained that chewing gum slowly was a good remedy, but it had to be American.

The Lid said his trick was the best. All you had to do was concentrate on a box of matches and at the same time recite the nursery rhyme - 'Little Bo Peep has lost her Sheep and doesn't know where to find them'.

'You can't be serious.' I gasped, shaking my head in disbelief.

I didn't fancy chewing gum or reciting nursery rhymes, but I understood their logic and decided to try something a little more sophisticated but along the same lines.

Only one man alive had the sheer power and untouchable magic to make me go the distance. Soon, his inspiration and mind-blowing commentating skills would solve my problem and have me going as long or short as each new situation demanded.

However, even after all my hours of practice in search of perfection, a photo finish was seldom within my reach.

In order to fine-tune my concentration, I had to revert back seven years to the halcyon days of 1960, when the magnificent Down team brought the Sam Maguire Cup over the border and 'up north' for the first time. The voice of Michael O'Hehir had always held me spellbound and instead of chewing gum or reciting nursery rhymes, I'd re-run the All-Ireland final in all its glory in my head. Once again, it was time to 'go over to Croke Park and the big match'.

'Go mbeannaigh Dia dhibh, a chairde, gaeil and welcome to Croke Park on this glorious September day for the All-Ireland Senior Football Final of 1960. The men from the Kingdom of Down meet the men from the Kingdom of Kerry and what a battle this promises to be, with the Down team being led out onto the field by their Captain, Kevin Mussen. For Down we have ... in goals, Eamon McKay, right full back, George Lavery, full back, Leo Murphy and left back, Pat Rice.'

My father took me to Dublin to see the match. He was a great Down supporter and, although I was born and bred in Fermanagh, I shouted for Down. 'Come on Down' I would shout, and, come to think of it, so did all the Down fans. Trying to shout something original, such as 'Give them the works boys', would have sounded out of place in a crowd of 90,000.

'And now to the full forward line, top of the right, Tony Hadden, full forward, Patsy O'Hagan and top of the right Brian Morgan. And here comes the Kerry team, dressed in the green and gold of the kingdom. In goals, Johnny Culloty, right full back, Jerome O'Shea.'

At this rate, I'll never see the throw in – hurry up, Sister.

'The players break rank and go back to their positions. The Artane Boys Band scurry off the field. The ball is thrown in and the game is on. The first to break away is Down. Joe Lennon side steps one man, he side steps two, he sends the ball, a short one to Tony Hadden. Tony Hadden hops it, he's going through, he's forty yards out, he's thirty yards out, he's still got the ball, he kicks it and yes! It's over the bar, the first score of the game and a point for Down.'

I wonder what Sister would say if she knew what I was thinking. Still, she seems happy enough, so it doesn't really matter what I'm thinking.

'The Down crowd going stark, starin', leppin', roarin' mad. From the kick out, a long, high ball drops into the centre of the field. The mighty Mick O'Connell goes up for it and plucks it from the air, he's robbed by Jarleth Carey. Carey sidesteps one man, then two, he's going toe to hand, he sells a 'dummy', taps it across to Joe Lennon, Joe Lennon's on the ball… he sends it to Paddy Mo…Doherty's on his own… he must score… it's, it's, it's into… No! No! No! It's hit the upright… and drifted… out over the end line and wide.'

'Sister… I… want… you… to… promise… me… you'll… never… bother… Maggie again… do you…

hear... me?'

'Yes, yes, Nurse Hanvey. Please keep going. Anything you say. Yes! Deeper, please, deeper.'

'I can't Sister, I'm Irish, and anyway I'm at the All-Ireland Fi, Fi, Final.'

She never heard me, thank God for that.

'Paudie Sheehy sends it over to Mick O'Connell. O'Connell grabs it from the air, he's robbed by Paddy Mo, Paddy goes toe to hand, he's covered ten, twenty, thirty, forty yards and he's still in control.'

I'm glad Paddy is for, I'm not.

'Doherty, a short pass to Tony Hadden, Hadden holds it on the hop, he passes to Joe Lennon, Lennon sends it over the heads of the waiting Kerry men, where it's intercepted by Paddy Mo, Doherty takes a kick and yes! It's, it's a good one, IT'S A GOAL, IT'S A GOAL, IT'S A GOAL FOR DOWN.'

With eyes locked and paralysed, she looked up at me and sighed drowsily.

'Hello, Nurse Hanvey.'

'Her right hand slowly caressed my face and then fell to her side like a brick from a building site. Unable to resist the temptation, I put on my best Michael O'Hehir accent and 'let go'.

'Hello, Sister and welcome to Croke Park on this glorious September day for the All-Ireland Final between Kerry and Down.'

'Are you right in the fucking head?' she snapped.

'Sorry Sister, I'm only joking.'

'Do you want to know something? It's twenty years

since I enjoyed anything like that' she smiled, as her warm hand ran down the entire length of my spine. Fine particles of chaff had combined to create little cigarettes of sweat, rolling and soothing. A bath was now not an option. It was a necessity. We sat upright on the edge of an overturned bale.

'Right Sister! It's time to talk. Promise me you'll leave Maggie alone and drop all the agro.'

'It's Maggie, Maggie, Maggie! Stuff Maggie! Do you realise that with all your Maggie-ing you nearly ruined that for me? I don't believe you do. You almost put me off!'

'Promise me, Sister. You just can't keep on doing this to her.'

'Nurse Hanvey, it's like this. I feel we are very good together and I need your company at this particular time of my life. See me whenever I want and I'll apologise to her tomorrow. Then things will return to normal.'

Taking my hands, her voice became motherly and full of warmth and understanding.

'Will you please listen to me, Bobbie, for heaven's sake and get some sense into that head of yours.'

It was the first time she used my name like this and it didn't sound right. I felt less comfortable with her.

'Listen, Nurse Maguire and you are simply not compatible. It's not only me - others have noticed this. The whole hospital's talking about you. She's not your type, and anyway she's a Free-Stater. I think you should get it over with, now rather than later.'

At first I thought she was lying. Then I had my doubts and I wasn't sure, but I loved Maggie and what anyone said didn't matter. I was hung, drawn and quartered and she knew it.

'That's not true. We are matched, Sister. You have no idea how we like being together. She's my one and only best friend and guess what? We're going to her house in Galway for the summer holidays. She lives in Cushla Bay. It's really beautiful.'

'Cushla my fucking Cree! Do you think I came out here tonight to listen to a geography lesson? Wait! Wait till I put on my coat. Get up! You're sitting on it! Come on, move! Oh! So 'we're' going to Galway now are we?' she mocked in a Southern brogue, 'What would she do if she saw you now?'

'Probably the same as Paddy, if he saw you now,' I countered.

'Put your clothes on before you catch cold.'

One minute she was nice to me, the next she was shouting and I couldn't understand why.

'Wait till you see what Sister's got in her big … coat … pocket, for her lovely Fermanagh madman.'

'I'm not lovely, Sister.'

'L-O-O-K!' she said, stroking the bottle as if it was a cat.

'What?'

'Only the best that money can buy, Black Bush.'

She took a long, noisy swallow and wiped her lips dry with the back of her hand.

Maggie was right. She was hitting it hard.

'I don't drink, Sister. When I was in England, I had some and I promised myself never to bother with it again. It's not nice, I don't like the taste of it.'

'Open your mouth you hypocrite!'

Standing over me, with her hand gripping my neck, she pulled me towards the bottle and tried to make me drink from it. Much of the contents spilled down my shirt and trousers and I jumped from the bale in anger and panic.

'I don't want it! I don't need it! It's not fair to Maggie.'

'Sit down, Nurse Hanvey. Let's begin again. Let me put it away. Here, let me wipe your shirt with my handkerchief.'

It was like treating a shotgun blast with a Band-Aid, but the way she touched me was nice.

'Can I see you again?'

'Yes, Sister.'

'Are you all right for money?'

'I'm all right.'

'OK, I'll talk to Nurse Maguire tomorrow and you'll see that will be the end of it.'

'Do you promise?'

'I promise. Now, put that cigarette out and hold me and if you ever get any of your Catholic guilt about us, remember I'm a Catholic too. Our church is an all-forgiving and all-embracing church. It teaches us one very important thing, God hates the sin but He loves the sinner. Now Nurse Hanvey, repeat! What does our church teach us?'

'God hates the sin but He loves the sinner, Sister.'

'That's a good boy.'

As she pulled me down into the hay once again, I could feel the tears building up in my eyes and Michael O'Hehir was only a memory.

The Ward

At the beginning of October 1968, I was transferred back to the psycho-geriatric block at Finneston House. It was becoming my home from home. Autumn was in terminal decline. Clouds were beginning to scud and the air carried the slightest hint of winter. Maggie had been in her usual good form during dinner and was looking forward to my birthday at Halloween. She said she'd already bought my present, 'You'll not like it very much, but you'll not be able to do without it.' I figured it must be a biology book or some other book that would come in handy for my exams.

The late shift ran from two to ten and at 1.30 pm I went into the ward, took off my jacket and put on my white coat. For the next eight hours and the next three months I would be in the 'heavy ward'. This meant the constant bathing of incontinent patients and the endless wheeling to and from toilet and bathroom. Gallons of the recommended disinfectant, Savlon, would spread its golden yellowness into oceans of tepid water, followed by the lifting in and out of overweight patients, some kicking and screaming and splashing and cursing and not wanting to go there. Hundreds of

Senokot, a powerful laxative, used to relieve constipation, would be dished out whether needed or not. 'Always keep the drains well flushed out', cried Bow Wow, the Charge. After this purging of intestines would come the inevitable blowouts. Once these depth charges got to work, we would be graced with wall-to-wall diarrhoea. Then more wheeling, more bathing and more drying, as hundreds of used towels waited in stuffed canvas skips for porters and the laundry. It never ended.

To be honest, I never really understood if patients were cleaned for their own benefit or if it was to make life more tolerable for the staff. Maybe it was a bit of both. Maloney always carried a fragrant aerosol in the pocket of his long, white coat to spray inmates who had dirtied themselves. The bigger the crime, the more they received. He hated shit so much, he even sprayed their heads. Standing with feet apart and hands tensed by his side he would shout, 'Go for your gun pilgrim', followed by 'Take that you ould fucker.'

A perfect line of ten, fully occupied, geriatric chairs were parked across the dayroom. When I said 'hello boys' only one answered. The others kept talking to themselves or arguing with their cigarettes. Carpet slippers, some wet and squelchy and sitting in a pool of nose-closing urine, tapped in time to the strange music being played on Radio Caroline.

'No! It couldn't be!' I looked and looked again and then walked towards him. I'd long forgotten he existed and had often hoped he was dead. I was about to confront my nightmare. He couldn't still be alive? Older and much fatter, it was him all right. He had taken on the appearance of a square block of lard and even the largest pullover looked tight and uncomfortable on him. Inactivity caused patients to grow into the size of their wheelchairs but seldom bigger, as though the designers had dictated their limitations.

That evil, oily peaked cap was pulled over his right ear, as if it hadn't moved in thirteen years. It was as I'd always remembered. This time, he wasn't smiling but looked deadly serious. After all, he was in a very serious place. No one had ever left Finneston alive. Patients admitted to Downshire thirty of forty years earlier were moved and transferred to various wards down through the years as their conditions progressed or didn't. This was the ward to end all wards. Eventually they would all end up in Finneston House, or as nurses called it 'Finishing House'. This was the end of the line - the gateway to eternity.

'Hello Bobbie,' he said.

'Well Fred,' I answered, 'and how are you?'

'I'm not so bad, not so bad at all, just not too good at the ould walkin'. They tell me it rained last night.'

'Yes, it did. And what has you in here?'

'Aw, there's nothing wrong with me.'

Oh aye, I thought, not another one. Would you believe it? Every one of them said that, even the psychopathic killers sent over from Rampton.

'I was livin' on me own, nowhere else to go. Not one to look after me.'

How the hell am I going to nurse him for the next three months? I wondered.

The thought of giving him an overdose or of even putting a pillow over his face crossed my mind - no one would ever know. If a doctor had examined a patient within the past six months there would be no post-mortem. According to our tutors, the most successful and cheapest way of killing a man was also the simplest. But, simplicity it seemed, was too basic for most homicides. In Ireland, shooting, strangling, stabbing and poisoning were the most popular methods. Killing a man was easy. All you needed was a syringe. Then you pulled back the plunger and filled it with air and the little bubble on the loose was guaranteed to kill and impossible to trace - invisible, like a pain in a vein.

As the days and weeks passed, Fred talked about the old days as if nothing had ever happened. Part of me hated him with an obsession and another part felt sorry that he should end up in Downshire. He looked and was helpless.

Two years later I was back again in Finneston, this time on night duty. After being briefed on the day's report, a staff nurse told me Fred was dying and asked me to sit with him during his final hours. I had done this on many occasions and had come to the conclusion that the act of death was over rated. 'Did he suffer much?' friends would ask me; 'No, not much,' I would reply, 'but he died smiling and it took the mortician two hours to remove the smile from his face.'

One old guy who had been very religious throughout

his life and who was one of the few who had nothing seriously wrong with him knew he hadn't long to go. He was obsessional about one thing.

'Straighten my teeth nurse, please straighten my teeth,' he would plead. He would then direct my thumb under his top plate and ask me to push upwards, 'Harder, push harder, oh please tighten it up, Nurse, you're not pushing hard enough.'

'Is that better? I'm pushing really hard. I don't want to hurt you Douglas.'

'You're not hurting me, Nurse, Go on, black, crack, clack it.'

'There Douglas, I've clacked it. It's tight now.'

After repeating this ritual for ten or fifteen minutes, he would let go of my hand and smile broadly, 'My smile's straight now, isn't it Nurse?'

If I refused to answer, he would panic: 'Nurse Hanvey, Bobbie, Mr Hanvey, look! Come closer, look! Is my smile straight now?'

'Yes Douglas, your smile is perfect, it's as straight as a die.'

'Get the mirror, Nurse, and we can check it together.'

'Sometimes he had me check his teeth for over an hour, but on his last night on this earth he had other things on his mind and I couldn't believe my ears. After a lifetime of condemning sinners, smokers and women, he tightened up that old smile and asked me to light him a cigarette.

'I'd like to taste tobacco,' he said.

I broke off the filter tip so he would get more nicotine, raised his pillows and propped him up.

'Here Douglas, it's easy, just pull as hard as you can.'

'You'll help me?' he asked.

'Yes, I will,' I replied.

Holding the fag to his lips, I watched him pull and puff and suck with a vengeance.

'Well Douglas, was that good?'

He straightened up that beautiful old smile once again and nodded, dropped his head to the side and was gone.

I took a night-light from the storeroom and placed it on Fred's bedside locker. Only when dying was such a luxury bestowed. I switched it on and trailed my chair over beside his bed. No relatives had come to say goodbye. He had none. His minister had called earlier and said all the prayers necessary for the passing. The next world, it seemed, cried out for and demanded perfection, just like this one. His oily cap sat sideways on his sweat soaked head. I vowed to steal it the moment he passed away.

The finger and thumb of his right hand kept plucking at the sheets that covered him. In an almost loving way, they searched and caressed the material as if counting threads or trying to decipher some hidden message. Our tutor had hammered home the point, 'always observe the patient who fumbles with his sheets.' This was one of the surest signs that the grim reaper was on his way. It's proper name was carphology, 'an involuntary picking at the bed-clothes seen in grave fevers or in conditions of great exhaustion'.

His lungs were rapidly filling up with fluid and every time he breathed a gurgling, crackling, almost fizzing sound told me he was burning up and all but done. The medical term for this type of breathing had a real scary ring to it that always reminded me of the chains of hell, 'Cheyne strokes'. Soon the death rattle would sound as the last remaining air was expelled from his body. Fred began taking in urgent, muffled gasps. Heavy words, scared beyond the point of recognition, tumbled from his mouth and his voice was barely able to carry them.

'Easy Fred, easy. For God's sake, slow down and take a breath. Take it easy. See! I've got your hand. Do you feel it? I'm with you. I'm not going away. And if you think I hold a grudge, well I don't, I'm no different than you were. Sometimes, I even think I am you – you were my friend and still are.'

He was not able to answer, but his hand tightened on mine in a final surge of energy, as if saying thank you and he was gone.

I tried to find a pulse but couldn't and closed his eyes, gently shutting out all light for the last time. It was 2 am, would you believe it? Two o'clock on my Tissot watch, what a time to die, why couldn't he have done it at daybreak like the rest of them? Twelve hundred patients were sound asleep in Downshire and Fred was dead. The barred sides of his white, metal cot-bed were released and lowered. He couldn't fall out and injure himself now.

I told the staff nurse I thought he was gone, because

as student nurses we weren't qualified to say one hundred per cent that a patient had died. This was the doctor's job, but sometimes if he was busy, or maybe if in bed after a busy day, he would ask the staff nurse who phoned him if he was sure the patient was definitely and absolutely dead. He would answer 'Yes' and would often have to repeat this message three times. If the patient wasn't absolutely dead before this lengthy phone call, then one thing was for sure, he was after it. Dying in Downshire was never a straightforward affair.

After the 'all clear' was eventually given, three of us washed and prepared Fred for his funeral, knowing the minister would ensure he received a proper burial.

Patients who had no relatives or friends were buried in hallowed ground belonging to the hospital. In a country where Protestants and Catholics were buried apart, it seemed strange that a common madness guaranteed they were laid in common ground. Our lonely plot was called Saint Dympna's after a young County Monaghan girl who became patron saint of the insane.

When my shift ended at seven, I felt exhausted and went straight to bed. I got up at two in the afternoon and took the bus the short distance to Fred's former home. I told myself this is where it would all finally end. Taking that old oily cap from my pocket, I tossed it onto the road in front of the cars, lorries and buses that soon thundered over it. For ten, long minutes I stood and watched as the big wheels churned it into the air. Sometimes taking on the shape of a giant swallow, it looped and soared before smacking to the ground again. Threads of raging rubber ate into its oiliness and spat it out with a venom that held me in awe. Soon realising that no amount of traffic could ever erase its memory, I left the scene, pleased at least I'd done what I set out to do.

The Ball

'Tap, tap, tap, tap…'

Up the long, dark hallway and down again, I bounced my leather football. When I got bigger, I'd play for our local Gaelic team. Goals would be my favourite position. I was good in goals. That way there was less chance of getting hurt in rough tackles. The boys from the mountain were as hard as nails and liked nothing better than seeing the ambulance arrive in the middle of a match. A photograph of the ambulance on the half way line in the local paper was sure to drive the fear of God into other teams in the parish who would be playing us at a later date. 'Nine years from eighteen leaves nine'; there was lots of time left for practice.

'Tap, tap, tap, tap…' up the hall and down again. On one of my solo runs, I noticed the bedroom door was just the teeniest bit open. Wheeling round, I stopped. As my left hand pushed it from me, my right kept bouncing the ball on the spot. 'Tap, tap, tap…'

His face was old and wrinkly and the colour of chocolate brought on by working outside in the summertime. I was pale and getting paler. My mates called me 'whitey'. This complexion gave the impression of being ill even when I wasn't and often came in handy when I wanted to stay off school.

She was looking up at him with a curious stretched look I hadn't seen before. The thirsty creak from the rusty hinge caused their heads to jerk in tandem as the ball hopped and tapped. 'Tap, tap, tap' on the green oilcloth. He smiled a silly, crooked smile as the sound of bouncing melted and mixed with the crunching mattress. She looked at me as if I wasn't there and although she saw me, I thought she hadn't. The yellow bedspread was gathered up his back and over his shoulders but I could see he was still wearing his jacket and overcoat. A skirt and blouse lay in a hurried pile on the floor. The collar of his shirt was black with the grime of engines. I hated dirty shirts, but the dirty thing that scared me most, was something I believed was never worn in bed. I couldn't keep my eyes of it. The peak of his flat, oily cap, which was pulled back on his head, pointed sideways over his right ear and pecked at me.

As pale hands gripped the lapels of his shiny, black coat, the bed moved and the ball bounced. My eyes danced backwards and forwards from the cap to the picture of Saint Theresa that hung on the flowery wallpaper behind them. I couldn't understand how a Protestant could be in the same room as Saint Theresa. Two o'clock on my Timex watch, two o'clock in the afternoon and the blind was pulled, but the sun shone through and made dark shadows. They weren't looking at me anymore. Still, that oily peak pointed.

Dropping the ball, I turned and fled.

Running wildly through the farmyard and across the fields, my bare scraggy legs clashed with the endless clumps of rushes as they slapped and chaffed my skin. I prayed they'd cut me in their thousands, yet had no idea why I wanted it to happen.

He had left his cigarettes, Gallagher's Greens, and matches on the table – he'd never see them again. Prizing the packet from the tight pocket of my short trousers, I sat down and lit up. It was the first smoke I'd ever had and it tasted good, but the picture of that oily cap just wouldn't go away.

Old Jim, the barman, had shown me how to make a little house out of rushes by weaving them together. I decided to make one. Two hours later it was four thirty and my house was complete. Although the sky was blue it looked grey. I said a prayer to Saint Theresa.

That Stormy Night

I pulled the big, heavy door of Finneston House behind me, locked it, checked it, and stepped out into the driving rain. My late shift was over. It had been a long, hard day, with most of the patients suffering from rampant diarrhoea and having to be bathed and changed over and over again.

Old Percy had broken all previous records having been washed nine times. He emphatically denied having the runs in the first place and kept insisting it was only sweat, brought on because the ward temperature had been turned up too far.

'Turn it off, Nurse. Aw, turn it off now,' he pleaded.

After lowering him down for the ninth time into his final soak in Savlon I felt like agreeing with him and almost believed the heating system could be faulty, which of course it wasn't.

I was jet-lagged, yet I hadn't flown an inch. Still, a good night's sleep would recharge the batteries and prepare me for more of the same tomorrow, the day after and the day after that. The bug, which caused so much destruction and dehydration in old people, usually stayed with them for three or four days at a time. There was still much work to be done.

Walking down the path from Finneston with the wind trying its best to turn me inside out, my hands fought with the hood of my anorak as I managed to pull it over my head, tie the toggles and, only just, keep on the move. It was one of those knee-length khaki coats which were popular during the sixties. Far from being waterproof, it gained weight by the second and never failed to flood the corridor in the Male Nurses' Home whenever I hung it behind the Sluice Room door. It was hopeless, but, at ten pounds, a bargain in its day.

I hated wearing it at any time, but more especially on rainy days when I envisaged being attacked and torn to pieces by a pack of mad dogs. In dry weather the circular strip of fur that decorated the front of the hood looked attractive in a funny sort of way, but when wet it reeked of rabbit, making me wonder how the manufacturers ever managed to overlook such an obvious health hazard.

The wind whined and mimicked the lonely cries of a sick child, as Maggie's voice tried to reach me, only to be blown back again and scattered into the night. Then a gentle hand rested on my shoulder.

'So you've had a rough day too, Hanvey?'

'Aye, indeed I did. It was diarrhoea all the way an' I'm totally and utterly exhausted. I just can't wait till my head hits the pillow.'

'It was the same in our ward. I've never seen it so bad. There'll be no peace for anyone on duty tonight,' she said wearily.

'It's always worse at night,' I agreed, 'and if someone happens to die before morning, it will be plain blue murder in there. They'll have to pull in extra staff. Maguire, I love you so much.'

'I love you too, Hanvey.'

We stopped walking and I kissed her. The wind pushed and pulled and shoved and did its best to drive us apart. She was beautiful and I told her so.

'Did you hear Nurse Flaherty's getting married soon?'

'To Billy?'

'Yes, they're a great couple, so well matched. I'm sure they'll be very happy together.'

'Just like us,' I smiled.

'Just like us, Bobbie Hanvey.'

'I want to hold you Maggie. I just want to hold you for the rest of my life.'

'Do you not think your arms would get sore?' she teased.

Well, that's a good question, I thought, and fought for time to think of an answer.

'I'd hold you till my arms dropped off.'

'And then, Hanvey, how would you hold me?'

'I'd, I'd, hold you with my head.'

'Aye, and it's big enough, that's for sure. Give me a kiss you big eejit, ye,' she smiled, as her wet hands touched my face and gently pulled me to her.

'It'll soon be that time of year once again, Maggie.'

'I love Christmas. Are you going to Midnight Mass?'

'Only if you're going.'

'We'll go together and we'll get dressed up,' she

enthused.

'But we always dress up for Mass.'

'I know we always dress up for Mass, Hanvey, but we'll make a special effort just for Christmas.'

The talk of Christmas and Midnight Mass released a happiness from deep within her that I had never witnessed before. It was beautiful. She loved her religion with a passion and in doing so, she loved and enjoyed life more.

'Everyone needs a focal point in their week,' she would say, 'and Sunday is that special day and without it every day is just the same.'

'One thing's for sure, there'll be no Connemara or Fermanagh for us this Christmas. I'm on duty. I've been asked to sing at a lot of ward parties, so there'll not be much real work done.'

'I'm on duty too. Will you be singing at our party?' she asked.

'I will indeed. I hope you're there when I come over.'

Gently squeezing my hand, she replied, 'I hope so too.'

'I hate staying in the female home at Christmas, it's like a morgue when everyone's away home with their families.'

'You could always come to some of the parties with me. It would help pass the time and sure you could always sing an ould song or two!'

'I'd love to Hanvey, if you don't mind, but there's one thing, I'll not be singing any songs.'

'Don't worry Maggie, we'll have a lovely Christmas.'

Crossing the road, we fought our way to the small green door in the high, ivy-covered perimeter wall, which reflected every bit of light it could find. Little heart-shaped leaves twitched and flickered.

It was as if the wall was moving, as we took careful aim with our shoulders and forced the small door back and jumped in, just before the wind slammed it angrily behind us and then roared over our heads from above. She was soaked to the skin and right before my eyes her uniform changed colour from light to royal blue.

Wet, rain-lashed hands caressed my face and diluted salt, as my broken whispers of sorry were heard over and over again and then her shaking words of comfort spilled over me, 'I'm sorry too, I'm sorry too.'

Dry matches scraped hopelessly on the damp sandpaper edge of a soggy matchbox and were quickly discarded until there was only one left.

The tall, frightened trees to the front of Downshire were even more scary on a night such as this. How they moaned and creaked, as rain-clad winds tore up the hill and over neatly kept lawns, before smashing their winter load onto the countless windowpanes of a million sorrows. Huddled on hunkers under her long navy blue cloak, we were drenched but warm and happy in this new castle of ours. Even though the nurses' homes were within vision only fifty yards away, we were for staying put in the trees.

Male nurses were not allowed in the rooms of female nurses. Female nurses were not allowed in the rooms of male nurses. This was the hospital policy and to break it would have meant instant dismissal. So, although the two homes were only thirty yards apart and we could wave to each other from our windows, or phone each other across, this was as far as it was supposed to go. Many staff broke the rules. Maggie did not.

'Hanvey, a half crown will do it.'

'Will do what?'

'Right. We have only one match left and if we strike it on the rough edge of a half crown, it should light and then we can have a wee smoke.'

Now that's brilliant thinking, I thought.

Timing was of the utmost importance. She put a cigarette in my lips and then her own and waited with quiet anticipation. Holding the coin tightly between her finger and thumb, I took the last match from the box and on the second attempt it flared. Her eyes smiled at me, as I raised the flame and watched the tobacco change colour and finally glow into a perfect red, circular dot.

The bright, scarlet lining of her nurse's cloak encased us like a womb, making us more warm and secure than we'd ever thought possible. We were content there, as Joe Dolan probably played a distant dance hall somewhere in the murky bogs of Ireland and as evil men in back rooms, with murder in mind, drew up plans for twenty-five years of bloody slaughter. These things were close to us, perhaps as close as twenty miles away, but we didn't know and cared even less.

She never spoke about politics. The happy times were

all that mattered. Her father, being a fisherman, was more concerned with fighting the sea to earn his daily bread. His job commanded him to face the sea and what was happening inland was just never that important.

Like her father, Maggie always faced the sea. She was the young student nurse still at odds with the Sixties, who refused to fall into line with the new 'freedoms' that had reached our country for the first time. Some said these new freedoms had come from America, but hundreds of years of the old Catholic ways were still firmly lodged in her brain, like countless splinters of fine jagged glass, each with a word written on it – words never to be used or tested. Pluck out any of these deadly messages at your peril and you immediately bled to death and drowned in thick, swirling rivers of blood.

In turn, my mind was overflowing with pictures of history and religion. They were intermingled and confused, but fully accepted just the same. Vivid scenes of lonely Mass Rocks, with cowering congregations hiding as resplendent Redcoats on prancing horses approached from the valley. Midnight Mass, with the sweet, hypnotic smell of slow, swinging thuribles, packed with smoking incense for Benediction, rosary beads, happy carefree days as an altar boy, endless guilt from breaking my Confirmation pledge at the age of ten and of stealing cider from the back yard of a neighbour's pub, the mumbling murmur of death prayers at the bedside, the pure, white immaculate vestments of the Parish Priest. He, my mother said, 'had the power to turn sinners like me into a pillar of salt.' So, if Maggie Maguire refused to allow me to make love to her, I would understand.

Men and women, all priests and nuns, who forever told the same story, had taught us an identical doctrine, It never changed, not even for a moment. In Dublin, Cork or Belfast, or the jungles of darkest Africa, the same story was being told. This was our story, we were part of the story, in fact we were the story. Maggie lived that story each and every day. She never missed Mass and made sure I didn't either. She learned, believed and saw it through, but I wanted to be different. I thought I could change it and add my own words, but all this had been tried before and never stood the test of time. Words flew past my ears like silent screams on scissors, as her long eyelashes froze in time, revealing sad, stunned circles of disbelief and despair.

The hem of her uniform was culled and tugged as her body turned in boxer fashion, head low to the waist, bobbing and weaving, but strangely remaining on the same spot and always keeping me at a safe distance. It reminded me of the first time in Finneston House, when our handshake lasted a lifetime, but was all too short.

Open fingers fended off unattractive advances, as the pounding rain ate our skin and spattered our vision. The clenched fist she did not know. The piercing cries of legions of lost souls condemned to madness in drably painted rooms exploded simultaneously in my head and pleaded hopelessly for me to stop, as the dead generations turned their heads in disgust and continued marching.

I was not what I seemed to be, or what I pretended to be, or even who I thought I was. For a while I was what I felt I wanted to be, only it wasn't me. I was so like her. I was basically good, but that was something I could never admit to myself. My heart simply wasn't with me this time. Lips tried to move and form new words of hope, but were paralysed. Our mouths parched, dry and finished. Fixed eyes waited anxiously for responses that never came.

It would be easy to patch things up. No great harm had been done, but I was somewhere low down on the graph of evolution. I could walk on the ground, but in reality it was only an illusion. Her eyes died on me, as the spark of happiness once within them was snuffed out, as a blessed candle was after Mass – that clearly defined, curling trickle of smoke, bending and wafting beautifully, but soon to disappear.

The memory of taking her on that old Ulsterbus to meet her father and mother all seemed so distant now. The thought of how happy she looked, when I shook hands with her parents for the first time in their West of Ireland home, made me wonder what was happening to me. Our hearts had burst with excitement as she raced me the two hundred yards down the long, cobble-stoned jetty to the wheelhouse of her father's boat, where the instruments gleamed and shone like diamonds, then inside to gaze through the little, red cabin window out onto the wild Atlantic. That was my most special present, the thought of which would stay with me forever. Heaven would never come much closer than this.

And now it was over.

Many years later and not so very long ago, our paths accidentally crossed for the first time since that night when the wind shed tears. The place was Mullingar, County Westmeath. I was there to take photographs of JP Donleavy and on the way home called into a shop for some cigarettes. Our Christian names, Maggie and Bobbie were used only once. There was no bullshit.

There was no 'You're looking great!'

There was no 'You haven't changed a bit!'

We were never into that stuff. We were so nervous of each other, we didn't know which way to turn. This time, no rosary beads fell from trouser pockets to keep conversation on flow, or no stones to be kicked with shining shoes. No beds lay in the shadows or locker in yellow, half-light, to create moods beyond imagination. It was the other side of a lifetime and I was on my own.

I spoke to her and she to me, only I couldn't hear her words any more. Frantically, I tried to grasp one or two, but they dissolved in mid-air. Customers passed us by, as travellers might at an airport, coming and going from every direction and none, hemming us in and adding to our confusion.

Sentiments were banished from thought, as we both failed to admit as to how it used to be. I wanted to apologise and give reasons, but they never came.

Our reactions to that chance encounter were

identical - complicated, bizarre and hazed, far beyond the point of reason. We were both in this thing together, whatever it was, and we wanted to run away. One thing, which I did vividly remember and will never forget, was her quiet, dignified, barely concealed hatred for me. It would prove to be the strongest and most sustainable that I would ever encounter. There was no exchange of addresses or photographs or telephone numbers. We parted as we had first met, all those years ago, when coming off duty – as strangers.

Her two children were beautiful.

Billy and the Holy Sisters

Nuns were not a common sight in a mental hospital, so when six of them breezed in and floated across the floor of Ward Forty-Nine, telling us they were there as a part of their training, we were flabbergasted. The sameness of the daily routine being broken, if only temporarily, pleased us and added to our sense of disbelief at having found ourselves in such 'heavenly' company.

As the hems of immaculately tailored garments clipped the highly reflective, machine-polished floor, they caused small puffs of dust to rise and swirl against the invading summer sunlight. As we watched, twelve clattering feet came to a standstill outside the permanently closed door of the Charge Nurse's office.

'Tap, tap, tap,' knocked the eldest.

'Come in Sisters, I've been expecting you, you're very welcome,' beckoned the Charge.

Each of them immediately and automatically fell into single file and said 'Thank you', as they slowly edged past him with heads bowed. Once again the door closed and the stout lock turned and clicked.

'Did you see that?' grinned my best mate Billy, as he spun full circle on the 'daggered' toes of his winkle-picker shoes. 'I wouldn't mind a night out with the wee fat one,' he beamed. 'I think she fancies me, did you see the way she looked at me?'

'Come on now, Billy, and stop imaginin' things and show some respect. Here's me thinkin' you're a Prod who doesn't exactly like Catholics and here's you wantin' to jump into bed with one of the Holy Sisters. Stop messin' and catch yourself on before it's too late.'

'I wouldn't mind introducin' the wee one to the Drum Major and givin' her a thump of the skin of the goat, while renderin' a verse or two of our glorious 'Sash',' he leered in his strong Belfast accent.

Pacing up and down, with his left shoulder dropped low, his hands in the flute playing position and throwing his left foot out a full ninety degrees, he started, 'Da da da, da, da, da, da, da da, and its colours they were fine.'

This was definitely the exact haunch and twist of an Orange flute player all right, the movements forever awkward but graceful in a menacing sort of way.

'Up Rangers,' he chanted and continued marching round and round in a never-ending circle. 'God bless Her Majesty the Queen, Gusty and the loyal heroes of the UVF and one hundred thousand Orangemen,' he saluted before snapping to attention and commanding me in a half bark to 'Dis…miss!'

'Billy, wise up. Do you honestly believe she'd look at you twice even if you weren't a Protestant?'

'Robert, old son, they like Protestants all right. They get an even bigger kick from us, because they think they've committed a bigger sin.'

'You're sick in the fuckin' head and whoever filled your head with all that shite is even sicker than you. There's no way she'd even consider goin' out with a wee Orange bastard like you.'

'Shusht,' he signalled, placing a long, first finger across his lips, 'shusht, they're coming back.'

A mass of blackness approached the frosted glass in the office door and it flung open.

'Good evening, Sisters, and youse are very welcome to Male Forty Nine,' he said in his broad East Belfast accent, curtsying and bowing too low for the occasion and acting as though he believed he was in Buckingham Palace.

I must admit he delivered his line beautifully and with a certain amount of respect, regardless of the shite that was packing his brain and had started to 'leak' a few minutes earlier.

'And good afternoon to you, Nurse, and thank you for such a lovely welcome, it's lovely to be here,' replied the eldest, who also happened to be the one he fancied. He grinned like a Cheshire cat and glanced in my direction, jerking his head sideways and winking with one eye at the same time. He was ecstatic.

'Hypocrite,' I whispered, but just loud enough for only him to hear, 'you're very welcome, Sisters.'

'Thank you, too, Nurse.'

The Charge then took the Sisters on a guided tour of the ward, introducing them to the patients.

'Good afternoon, Sisters,' I mimicked after they were gone, in a broad Belfast accent, bowing low and backing back like a Chinaman. 'You must be about the worst Protestant I've ever come across, Billy.'

'What the hell do you mean?'

'Well, one minute you're wantin' to introduce her to the Drum Major and the next it's 'Good evening Sisters'. I wish you'd make your stupid mind up. If your friends in the Orange ever get to hear about this, then your days of marchin' to the 'Field' at Finaghy will be well and truly over. They'll throw you out in disgrace and you'll probably end up joining the military wing of the Legion of Mary.'

'Your're not tellin' me now that the Legion of Mary have got a military wing?'

'Did you not know that?'

'No, I did not,' he answered abruptly.

'So there y'are now, that's a new one for you to raise at your next Lodge meeting,' I teased.

'Oh,' he replied, pretending not to be interested.

'It's well known in these parts, that they do their training in the Mourne Mountains at weekends,' I assured him.

'You're jokin'?'

'No I'm not. They're trained to kill all right, but very slowly, using a technique that's more horrific than the Chinese Water Torture.'

'And what technique would that be?'

'They beat you to death with a wet lettuce,' I cheered.

'Hanvey, you're one rotten Fenian bastard,' he raged and threw a few friendly punches at my shoulder, which soon hurt like hell.

The Blotter for her Eyes

The next day, the good sisters were dispersed throughout the hospital, taking up their new positions in various wards. My favourite from the word go was Sister Terrifica, at least that's what I christened her on our first day on duty together. Days soon disappeared into weeks and as her presence moulded into the shifts, her mystery heightened and my interest in her became intense.

I was forever teasing her how I would one day 'get her out of her habit', but she only replied in all seriousness, 'We'll have to pray together soon, Bobbie'. My answer was always the same: 'It would be a pleasure to pray with you any time, Sister Terrifica'. She always laughed at this, making me wonder if she believed I was serious. I thought I was, but sometimes I wasn't so sure.

Nuns, she told me, were taught to avoid having eye contact with others, and when out walking would look straight ahead at all times. Left and right simply weren't part of their geography. At every given opportunity after that, I would stare her out for minutes at a time, my own eyes sinking deep into her dark, sad pools. Her embarrassment was so visible, I could almost touch it. She was covered from head to foot in the old uniform of nuns, with only her face showing as if in a death-mask. She undoubtedly looked the part of the deeply religious, caring person she was, but her eyes told me something different, although I couldn't figure out exactly what that was; there was a barely controlled wildness about them.

Her eyebrows, like two perfectly drawn arches of soot, were the richest, purest black I had ever seen. The whites of her eyes annoyed me with their brightness, so much so I could never see enough of them. Full, pale lips cried out for a blood transfusion or the colour of anything, even lipstick. In reality she was a black and white photograph.

One day, we knelt and prayed together before one of the patients came into the ward and startled us. I was hypnotised by her pale almost transparent fingers and by the way her rosary beads hugged them, as if raindrops clinging to a summer rose. Some weeks later, the ward deserted, we sat by the electric fire. It was early afternoon and the patients were either at occupational therapy or in the Sugar Bowl.

The floor in the dormitory area was the shiniest in the entire hospital. Rows of neatly made beds lay in wait as small, tidy lockers stood smartly to attention. Sitting in two very low but comfortable chairs, I casually asked her, 'What age are you now, Sister?'

'Twenty-seven,' she replied, 'and what age are you?'

'Twenty four and a half. If you had to do it all over again, would you still be a nun, or would you have chosen a career in nursing?'

'In the County Sligo, where I come from, all the girls become either nurses or nuns, or emigrate to England or America, there's no work at home for us. But to answer your question, yes, I'd still be a nun. What would you have been had you not become a nurse?'

'Well Sister, in the County Fermanagh, where I come from, all the boys become either nurses or... nuns. I think I'd have become a nun, Sister.'

She smiled a puzzled smile of disbelief, turning her head from me as she did.

'Seriously, I'd probably still be working in a factory. I left school at fifteen or rather, the vice-principal, Mr Hughes, told me to 'consider' leaving and never to buy a motorbike. I was never able to figure out exactly what he meant by that.'

'Perhaps he thought you'd kill yourself.'

'You're right. That's exactly what he meant. It's funny, but I never thought of that before.'

'Sure, it's impossible to think of everything Bobbie.'

'That's true Sister, that's very true indeed. Do you not become very uncomfortable, especially during the summer, wearing all those clothes?'

'Oh, you mean my habit?'

'Yes.'

'Yes, it does become extremely hot, but rules are rules.'

'And is your hair long under your head-dress?'

'It almost reaches my waist, but I'm having it cut soon.'

'Will you keep me a little piece when you do?'

As if speaking her thoughts aloud, she whispered, 'Am

I hearing this?' and then softly continued, as her eyes rolled with some embarrassment, 'We'll see'.

'Sister, can I say something?'

'If you must,' she answered, again staring into the cold, grey bars of the turned-off electric fire and adding, 'sure nothing has stopped you yet!'

'You're very beautiful for a nun.'

'And you're extremely ugly for a nurse.'

'Sure, good looks aren't that important anyway, Sister.'

'You're right, of course they're not, ' she smiled trying to lessen my discomfort, which was now causing me to focus on the sparkling chrome, wall-mounted fire.

'Bobbie, always remember the good Lord giveth and the good Lord taketh away and in your case when he was handing out the good looks, he certainly did his fair share of taking away,' she laughed.

'Very, very good Sister,' I dryly stammered and continued gazing at the fire.

My father used to tell me that a favourite traditional Irish pastime was sitting in chairs and gazing or spitting into fires. We were no better than cats, he would say, fascinated with fires, fires on the brain. If I had been one hundred per cent sure of not getting electrocuted, I'd have turned it on and spat into it, just for badness. My father also insisted that most people who were found dead in chairs in front of fires, probably spat into them minutes before they had passed away, but the only manner of proving that they had actually spat would have been if they'd missed. My father was some character all right.

Out of the corner of my eye, I could see Sister was still smiling and twiddling with her rosary.

'Did you know Bobbie, that the good Lord carries each and every one of us in the palm of His hand and when someone falls off, that's when they die.'

'Get away,' I said in disbelief, but also failing to grasp the magnitude of such a theory.

'When you think about it carefully you'll discover it makes sense,' she added.

'Sister, why do you keep looking away?'

'We're not supposed to have eye contact; I told you that earlier.'

'But we had good eye contact five minutes ago.'

She never answered and kept gazing at the wall.

'I love your eyes so much, little Sister, can I please look into them just one more time?'

Quickly turning round, she opened her eyes as wide as she possibly could, stretched her skin by pulling a funny face, gaped at me intensely for all of two seconds and glanced away again.

'There you are now, was that all right,' she smiled mischievously, in her infectious Southern brogue.

'That's not funny.'

'I thought it was very funny,' she laughed. 'Please forgive me for being flippant, but something came over me and I just couldn't he … hel … help it,' she giggled, before bursting into an uncontrollable fit of laughter.

Still, it was nice to see her so happy, even though I'd never seen a nun do that before. In an instant, sadness replaced merriment as her face lowered and her eyes blankly searched the mirrored shine on peeping shoes. Delicate fingers that cried out to be touched, fidgeted nervously with the unending span of beads and twisted the chain to breaking point. It was as if every ounce of energy in her body was trying to escape, but had no idea of where to go.

Her head started to rise and the darkest, deepest hovering eyes swung in my direction, met mine, clicked into position and stayed there. Her lips revealed a barely visible tremor and prepared to move.

'Bobbie, let me put it like this, if I admired men, which I do not, you would certainly not be my first choice of friend,' she said, though not unkindly.

She sure knows how to get even, I thought.

'But having said that, you are the only person I've ever met who made me feel so good about myself and treated me as something other than I am. In fact, you make me feel too good about myself. You have begun to make me question my vows. I greatly admire your high spirits and zest for living, but all of this is wrong. I really enjoy your company but I'm going to request a change of ward so I won't be with you anymore.'

'Sister, may I now tell you how you make me feel? If it means anything to you, I…'

'Please tell me,' she interrupted.

'This is going to be difficult, but here goes anyway,' I said, throwing caution well and truly to the wind.

'Go on,' she said, making me feel as if I was isolated and entombed in the silent, black world of the confession box for the first time. The racing tick of the ward's electric clock unnerved me, compounding my uncertainty.

My old friend Joe Stratton compared the way life changed to the ticking of two clocks. The old 'wag of the wall' came from an age of caring and relaxation and everything about it, from the way it was made to the way it looked, oozed class at every chime. Its tick was slow, deliberate and almost hypnotic as it told us to, 'Tick your time, tick your time, tick your time'. On the other hand the modern electric clock looked like plastic, as if it was made in a hurry, which it was. It had neither class nor respect, but its tick, which was repeated furiously, told us to 'Get up and get at it, get up and get at it, get up and get at it'. I loved Joe's story of the two clocks.

'Every day and night I think of you, Sister Terrifica. I purposely go to bed to think of you and wonder if all of you is as white as your hands and face. If so, I want to die in your whiteness. Your face looks over me from the darkness and protects me. Your eyes forever cut me like razor blades, without mercy and I never want them to stop. I want so much to share your loneliness.'

Taking her right hand, which in turn was clutching her rosary, my finger circled her wrist and moved to the inside where her pulse was dancing so fast it was impossible to count the beats. The blood was gushing in her veins. Mixed up fingers soon became trapped in the beads and added to her consternation. 'Sister, I long to kiss your skin and hold you and tell you how much I love you. I know it can never happen but at night when I'm alone, it does happen.'

Her eyes became blurred, as a tiny tear slowly sliced her skin and came to rest on the corner of her mouth. I removed it with the tip of my finger and tenderly placed it on my tongue.

'Now, I carry part of you with me Sister. You taste beautiful.'

Her eyes filled up and became wet and swollen. As I raised her hand to kiss it, she hurriedly jumped from the chair, stepped back from me and cried, 'Stop! Stop! Please stop!'

Turning round, she swung right and stormed up the long corridor of echoes with her habit moving as I'd never seen it move before. I heard the familiar jingle of keys and then seconds of silence as she selected the right one. The heavy lock clicked and the cloakroom door closed solidly behind her and the lever turned yet again.

A long fifteen minutes passed before the sound of unlocking and locking was repeated. The almost inaudible swish of garments grew louder and in seconds she was standing over me.

'Please take a seat Sister,' I nodded.

'No thank you, I'll stand if you don't mind and I'll still stand if you do. Bobbie, I must say goodbye,' she said coldly, 'I would like you to have these.'

Her now open, outstretched hand revealed a small rosary with a cross of beautifully cut, sea green glass that made the crucifixion almost come alive.

'These touched the image of Our Lady of the Americas,' she said, 'and will bring you everything that is good and what you wish for in life.'

As they tumbled into my hand, her fingers slowly recoiled into her palm and she took one step back.

'Goodbye, Bobbie,' she whispered.

I never answered her or looked up, but instead gazed transfixed at the rosary and repeated the most beautiful sounding name I'd ever heard, 'Our Lady of the Americas'. Carefully dropping them into the top pocket of my white coat, and throwing my feet up onto the electric fire, I tried to convince myself that the last hour had actually happened.

The next day she was transferred, at her own request, to another ward and didn't return to Male Forty-Nine. After that I often saw her walking and praying in the grounds and sometimes in the canteen but we never spoke. I told myself that I had committed a big sin and they didn't come much bigger than this. In fact, this was possibly the worst, but I felt as though I'd really done nothing at all. An old fire and brimstone preacher who came to our annual mission in Brookeborough when I was nine or ten told us it was possible to commit a mortal sin by just sitting in a chair and thinking 'bad' thoughts. He said you could be blindfolded, bound hand and foot, gagged, ear-plugged and tied in chains and still be able to commit a mortal sin, so on this occasion at least I felt I fitted into that category. But, I wanted so much to share her loneliness, and I was fully prepared to face the ever-lasting flames of hell just to hold her close. I wanted to be the blotter for her eyes.

The Visitor

Some time later, I was on night duty, going to bed around eight o'clock in the morning and getting up about four in the afternoon. It was the middle of winter and strangely enough almost on the doorstep of Christmas once again.

Something stirred me and I woke. Trying desperately to focus, my eyes struggled and gazed in total bewilderment through the open, blue door onto the narrow, dark landing, which was poorly lit from the glow of a bare sixty-watt bulb.

It was one of those landings that had been painted so many times, the walls had gained a texture all of their own. Purple was the latest addition, being a popular colour at the time. Everything was covered in it, but I still loved that battered, dying, old flat. It was home.

In awe I stared in disbelief, not knowing exactly where I was, or what she was doing there. It was as if I was the only witness in the whole world to this rare, beautiful vision – my everlasting photograph of unending mystery.

A long, black habit revealed the shining tips of two resting shoes. Gaunt and ghostly, but in a way which caused no dismay, she calmed my initial shock like an anaesthetic, making me feel no need to panic and content at being covered by her stillness.

Desolate, never-blinking eyes caught the light from the sixty-watt and hurled it through the darkness in my direction, sending messages that stirred me from head to foot.

A heavy silver and black crucifix which was jammed at an angle like a six-gun, behind her broad, brown belt occasionally glinted as if trying to sedate me.

Her hands were hidden up opposite sleeves.

My hand moved quietly under the blankets as her eyes were glued to mine. Fixed in the hypnotic stare of death, they held me spellbound from a distance of some ten to twelve feet.

Then I heard it! The thump, thump, thump of hurried footsteps running up creaky old stairs.

My hands quickly abandoned the stored warmth of the bedclothes and met the cold, winter air of the chilled room for the first time in eight hours. The old, battered alarm clock said 'ten to four'.

I signalled with great urgency to warn her of the coming danger but, as if in a trance, she stood statue-like, never flinching or batting an eyelid. Her long rosary hung motionless by her side.

Suddenly a voice cried out, 'How did you get in here? Who let you in? Get out! Get out! Who do you think you are? Get out! You're not wanted here!'

Her eyes remained fixed on mine, as if eating the last meal they would ever see. She never spoke or made a sound.

Then, in complete silence, she slowly turned and was gone. I never saw her again.

The Dream

Having neglected my religion for many years, I was amazed at how my mind had stored the faith of my childhood, a faith I thought I'd forgotten, until I dreamt. A recurring dream I had of my own death should have been a frightening experience, but it wasn't. Like a re-run of an old movie, it never changed and continually showed the conflict and turmoil within me, as I struggled to speak her name for the last time.

Stout, big-breasted women, with ruddy complexions, strong arms and lost opportunities, long since impervious to their husbands' drinking and pawing, were now towering over me and collectively gathered around my bedside as good caring members of the local branch of the Legion of Mary.

So, relieved at being away, even temporarily, from the sickly rush of their partners' breath, they never noticed the cloud of approaching death, already surrounding them.

Burning candles helped to purify the putrid air, as decade after decade of the rosary was whispered in murmurs, in respect for the last of the human senses to fade. Prayers of every description, most of them known to me, were repeated furiously, but now and again a special one, which I'd never heard before was driven at urgent speed in my direction. These were the heavyweights the priest had given them just for the night, to be returned by daybreak when it was all over.

These special prayers would add weight to last minute efforts in agreeing a plea bargain with the Almighty, in order to get 'this old sinner' a reprieve from Hell or, at the very least, a short term in Purgatory – probably ten to fifteen years, if successful!

It was known as the place for lost souls, where the fire was just as hot as the one in Hell, but after doing your time there, you were released, so there was light at the end of the tunnel. It had a fairly good reputation and I was never frightened of being sent there.

I always believed that going to Heaven would be wonderful, but it gave me one very serious worry – the finality of it all! After Heaven, there would be no more places to go. No more travelling, rambling or magical mystery tours. Once you were fortunate enough to get there it was, quite definitely, the end of the road.

Curious, shifting shadows quivered on low praying faces, with erect arms clutching busy rosary beads, as tired elbows rested on the brilliant white sheets, so lovingly arranged on my bed. From one time to the next they would be respectfully wrapped in brown, greaseproof paper and stored in dark drawers, where the light of day could never touch them, usually in the bottom of a wardrobe and below pyjamas, which were only taken out in times of sickness.

I could recall from my nursing days, that most patients died between five and seven in the morning when the body was at its lowest point of resistance. This, too, would be my time.

I tried to smile, but the little veins and arteries were saying they couldn't keep me going for much longer. They were becoming blocked, broken and hopeless and I slipped out of consciousness for a few seconds.

On coming round again, the whisper of praying voices had changed to a constant, purring drone, the same sound made by the air conditioning in Finneston House when I first met Maggie all those years ago. Then, for no apparent reason, things became extraordinarily clear and sharp again.

Cotton-wool buds, loaded with freshly diluted Savlon were peeling through layers of caked, foul-smelling mucus on parched lips, now trembling and useless. But those same lips had nevertheless, tasted the fresh sweetness of her summer breath, back in the days when all this old dying 'stuff' was never even contemplated.

In the next room just beyond the prayers, relations gathered for the waiting. Prim, straight-laced ladies who nodded more often than they spoke, wore those bee-hive hats and sat with poker straight backs. The constant adjusting of hemlines just that one quarter of an inch or so, ensured respectability as they quickly eyed the men folk to see if they'd noticed the difference. It was in places like these that 'matches' were made.

My eyes, sunken and starry now, saw nothing and a

lonely tear escaped, slowly making its last, long journey down the side of my face, cutting a cool refreshing swathe through the thick sweat of death.

A hundred voices in perfect unison began to recite the rosary, led by those good women in the front. Those good women of the Legion of Mary would soon leave the house and walk or drive to their own homes. There, husbands would enquire as to why they'd stayed so long. They would ask the names of the men-folk at 'the wake', just to check the presence of 'randiness' in the assembly on a scale of one to ten. That might or might not, help to instil some 'peace of mind'.

Very soon, those holy women would return to the smell of stale Guinness and last minute orders in the bedroom. They would once again pretend, by saying the right words at the right time and sighing and moaning on cue, as their husbands drove it home, calling them names they didn't know on their wedding day.

Life was one funny old excursion, but my 'bus' was pulling up to the 'terminal' for the last time. The frantic rubbing of my hands slowly changed to a touch so gentle I wondered who on earth it could be - could it be her?

No, there would be no possibility of that. It was too long ago. That was at the other end of a lifetime.

Any minute now, rosary beads would be dropped back into pockets, prayer books carefully placed in handbags and candles blown out. Sheets would be draped over mirrors in the battle against evil and clocks stopped at the exact moment of my departure. Aerosols of captured fragrance, stolen from the lilac, pine and every other flower and tree in the forest, would be hissed around the room before the breeze from the open windows gradually diluted the mix and restored a healthy, normal freshness once again.

Then the holy water rained over me. It was gentle and welcome, like a summer shower cooling me for the longest journey I would ever take.

Sleeping with Butterflies

Tara strode over and sat at my table. Her lips cut a pencilled line of pain, but only for a second, then it was gone. Soon, she relaxed again. I could feel her inhaling. Eyes deeper than a bottomless pit tried to read me. She was the epitome of darkness.

'Tea?' I beckoned, thinking there might be a good possibility of asking her out. Many of the boys in the home had tried. None had succeeded.

'No thanks, I've had some.'

'Did you get my message?' she asked.

'What message?'

'Never mind, do you realise this country's about to explode?' she enthused, as if she couldn't wait for it to happen.

'Is it?'

'How would you like to swap your white-coat for camouflage and come with me to Dundalk at the weekends?'

'What for?'

She covered the side of her mouth with a strong hand and whispered: 'Weapons training'.

'Christ! you've got to be joking. Who are we supposed to kill?' I asked in amazement and disbelief.

'Any fucker stupid enough to get in our way - we have more guns than fingers to pull them. What d'ya say Fermanagh?'

'Marching for civil rights is one thing, shooting at someone is another; I couldn't do that. Count me out.'

'It's as simple as taking your first drink, after that you'll be a fully-fledged alcoholic. There's fifty armalites and five thousand rounds of ammunition in the tunnels below Downshire.'

'You shouldn't have told me that, I don't want to know.'

'And now that you do know, what are you going to do about it?'

'I never heard it.'

'Oh yes you did!'

She had put me in an impossible situation and had done so purposely. If, indeed, there was stuff in the cellars and if the police found it, I wondered would the IRA blame me for tipping them off?

'Tara, you fight the war if you have to. I'm thinking of going into photography. The only thing I aim to aim is a camera.'

'Don't forget to keep her loaded. We'll make sure you get plenty of work. Before long you'll think you're in fuckin' Vietnam. Oh! Incidentally, I hear your Maggie is emigrating to England. If you don't mind me saying so, she'll marry some cockney bloke and you'll never see her again. You have my deepest sympathy. Take care.'

'Oh, how do you fancy going to the hayshed?' I edged.

'I don't think your balls are big enough.'

On that sour note, she smiled a superior, snaked smile and went back to her table. The confidence she oozed was unsettling and the words 'take care' had the tone of pure threat written all over them. Tara seemed to be the business all right. All the signs pointed to a long nightmare of something that was already on its way.

Why did she mention Maggie?

Three months later, Moriarty phoned and said she wanted to see me.

'Maggie said to say goodbye. She left for England yesterday to do her General Nursing. I wish I was away with her.'

So do … I stopped myself in mid-sentence, 'Was that all she said?'

'That's the complete message.'

'What were her exact words?'

'Tell Hanvey I said goodbye.'

'Is her room empty?'

'I should hope so.'

'Was she happy leaving?'

'Come on! What do you think?'

'How do you fancy coming and getting drunk with me?'

'I'll see you home safe.'

For weeks, I tossed her answer 'Come on, what do you think?' around in my head and could make no sense of it. I wondered why she'd bothered to say goodbye after the way I'd treated her. Did this mean she still loved me? In primary school, old Barney McCusker used to say, 'Too late, too late, shall be the cry'. I was out of tune with myself. There was nothing left to lose.

The next Saturday, it was Armagh's turn to have a civil rights' march. Every Saturday the venue changed. The weekly phone call to the Northern Ireland Civil Rights' Association told me the slogans to print on this week's placards from the Downpatrick branch. Every week the slogans changed, but all posters at demos carried identical slogans. Revolutions had to be co-ordinated. On one occasion I got word that a hospital in County Tyrone was staffed with almost one hundred per cent Catholic workers and very few Protestants. Testing the theory of civil rights to the letter, I phoned HQ and informed them of this fact. Their reply, 'Oh I think you'd better forget about that,' surprised me, but confirmed my belief that there was more to propaganda than a clever slogan.

I stood before the judge in Downpatrick Court on three occasions, usually for Riotous Behaviour. After being fined ninety pounds, I went to Belfast to collect money to pay the court.

'How much did they do you for?' asked Frank the dentist, a gentle quietly spoken man, who was one of the association's most genuine organisers.

'Ninety pounds.'

'Right, here you are,' he counted, 'eighty, eighty-five, ninety. Always remember we can pay your fine, but we can't do your time.'

'My friend was fined ninety pounds as well.'

'It's a good job this money comes from America. Hold

out your hand. There now. Are you sure that's enough?'

'Yeh, that's fine.'

'What did they do you for?'

'Riotous Behaviour.'

'Such as?'

'Kicking a cement lorry in Ardglass. The scabs were bringing it in on boats from the Irish Republic and the driver tried to run over our sit-down protest on the quay.'

'Ardglass! That's right, I heard that lorry had a slight 'accident' on the border.'

'I didn't hear that,' I said and had no desire to learn the details. 'That was my second time in Ardglass. On my first visit there I slept with a butterfly.'

'Keep up the good work.'

'Sleeping with butterflies?'

'No, kicking cement lorries,' he laughed.

I had never come closer to landing in jail. When the court ended, I asked a policeman why they never prosecuted the leaders of the movement instead of the rank and file. It took me some years to understand his answer.

'Sure, if we jailed those boys, do you think chappies like yourself could keep all this excitement going?' He added, 'You'll never get them to riot in Downpatrick, their mother's won't let them out.'

The Downpatrick police had gained the reputation of being the most successful in Northern Ireland when it came to scooping activists and gunmen. I soon learned that placing my life in the hands of local sympathisers would be suicide. There was more to being Irish than wearing a shamrock or an Aran sweater and smoking a pipe. No one had told them. I had already made up my mind to quit.

The big march in Armagh was being held to commemorate the first anniversary of the death of John Gallagher, shot dead by the Tynan B-Specials, a part time police force. The atmosphere was crackling. Two or three steps in front of me, I saw a member of the Special Branch who fitted in perfectly and looked like any other protestor. He used to call at Downshire to find out when the next rally was due to be held in Downpatrick. He was a decent friendly man who was only doing his job. Some years later he was killed in car crash on the Ards Peninsula.

On my far left, the street was sealed off with a solid block of uniforms, riot shields and batons at the ready. I thought it was the most beautiful sight in the world.

I loved looking at it. The tension in the air was visible. Dr Ian Paisley and two hundred of his followers roared and jeered in our direction, clearly spoiling for a fight. I was glad they were behind the police line and that it held fast, even though civil rights leaflets told us 'how to disarm the police'.

After listening to a torrent of fiery anti-government speeches from the steps of a building, which I'd probably never recognise again, I spotted 'busy' men milling and working the crowd. They talked briefly to some protesters before moving on briskly and selecting others. Suddenly one approached me. His expression was unforgettable. Here I was, wondering if it would be possible to hitch a lift from the area without getting a kicking. At meetings like this, Ian Paisley's followers weren't out to win any citizen-of-the-year awards. This guy had no such worries. Smiling all over the place his warm breath tickled my eardrum, 'Would you like to come to Dundalk or Donegal for…' I could hear his words running in unison with Tara's '… for weapons training.'

Jesus! I thought, Tara was the real McCoy after all.

'No thanks, I'm working, I wouldn't have the time.'

Before I could finish, he was going and asking somebody else. He was gathering up cannon fodder to help stock the graveyards of Northern Ireland. He was definitely enjoying his work. This was my last civil rights march. Things were in top gear and moving much too fast for me. I could now see the thing that was coming. It frightened me.

In the General Office, I leaned over the big desk. The duty officer sat opposite twiddling with a form and a pen.

'Sign here and I'll sign after you,' she said coldly.

The form read:
FOR ITEMS RETURNED.

Hospital Keys	Sign here.
White Coat	Sign here.
Nursing Books	Sign here.
Key to your Room	Sign here.

The decision to leave nursing wasn't an easy one. It wasn't difficult either.

You Should Never Go Back

There it was again, just as I'd remembered. Unchanged and unforgiving. Brooding and lurking back at me through a ragged curtain of ancient beech trees. An endless mountain of red brick, stretching and towering in the cold November sun.

When I first gazed in disbelief at the old place it was almost thirty years ago, but, no matter how hard I concentrated, the magic of yesterday and all the energy it inspired was gone forever. Trying to call it back again was hopeless and pathetic.

Age, the great reducer in the size of things, was helpless when it confronted the sheer power and awesome physical landscape that was Downshire Mental Hospital.

Even after all this time, it still possessed the cunning and psychopathic charm to confuse, confound and manipulate but never once failed to impress. Something compelled me into returning for one last time, to smother myself in memories and be close to someone who wasn't there anymore.

Down eight concrete steps to my left the same two flagged pathways cut through the lawn, and led to the nurses' homes. This had been my base of contentment and self-imposed turmoil for six of the most interesting years of my life.

A young nurse, wearing a look of distant vagueness that contradicted her lack of years, passed me as if veiled from the world.

'Excuse me, Nurse?' I called after her.

'Yes, may I help,' she smiled, turning and walking confidently towards me. Her broad smile, soft and sensual, was identical to one I'd known as a rather green student fresh in from the bogs of County Fermanagh. I told myself it was merely coincidence but the striking resemblance bothered me just the same. It simply couldn't be.

'Do many students live-in these days?' I asked.

'None, only me. It's like a morgue in there. It gives me the creeps. I'm thinking of moving out,' she answered with a shiver.

I'd heard that comparison only once before but it always stayed with me.

'And over there,' she pointed, 'the Male Home is now the Alcoholic Unit'.

'It always was, wasn't it', I joked and she laughed appreciatively.

'Yes, my mother mentioned something like that. You're Mr Hanvey, aren't you?'

'Yes. Bobbie.'

'Well, she still rattles on about the old days and I hear your name cropping up from time to time. This must have been some place in the Sixties. She said you were good friends.'

'Good friends? Were we? What's her name?'

'Theresa O'Flynn.'

'You don't mean Sister O'Flynn?'

'Yes, the very one.'

'Oh my God!' I said to myself. 'God hates the sin but He loves the sinner', the war cry of a tortured Catholic and Sister O'Flynn's slogan in life. It gave her peace of mind after encounters which were totally at odds with her religion.

'And your name, Nurse?' I asked, cringing the cringe of immediate discovery. The forgotten thirty-year gap was falling into place with the speed of an electronic jigsaw puzzle. I saw her lips move as if in mime but never heard an answer.

She was her mother's daughter all right and no mistake about it. That visible scent of darkness lured thoughts almost to the point of words, and it was clear that the old magic had now filtered down into the new generation.

But those green eyes, that nose and those broad shoulders that cried out for the touch of silk, were the exact features that had survived in our family for generations. Once again I told myself I was imagining things. If she accused me, I'd deny it. I'd blame the breadman and if my back was really to the wall, then I'd blame the priest or better still the curate.

The feel of her fingers tapping my shoulder startled me in much the same way as a bee does when it crashes into the side of your face.

'Are you all right, Mr Hanvey?'

'I'm sorry Nurse. I must have been day dreaming again. Some say it's the forerunner to Alzheimers'. I suppose you've already heard about the Irishman with Alzheimer's'?'

'No, but I have a feeling you are going to tell me.'

'He forgot everything but still hated the British.'

'Aye,' she laughed, 'there's plenty of boys like that around.'

'We're completely and totally surrounded.'

'Before I forget, my name's Molly and I'm very pleased to meet you,' she enthused with a firm handshake, which lingered that little bit too long.

'And I'm pleased to meet you Molly. What age are you now?'

'Twenty-seven in October.'

Christ! February! During the big snowstorm, I quickly calculated, no, it couldn't be. Surely, Sister would have told me. Someone would have told me, or maybe, again, they wouldn't. The Irish were a useless bunch when it came to giving you the tip off, especially if your life depended on it. An old timer once told me, 'they'd watch you drown before they'd let water touch them.'

'And your mother, how is she these days?'

'Oh she's fine. She's retired now for quite a few years. I must tell her I was talking to you. You're a photographer, isn't that right?'

'That's right. Half of my life is spent in the darkroom, but I wouldn't change it for the world. I enjoy it very much and anyway it's easier to keep than a pigeon loft.'

'I know exactly what you mean,' she winked, 'my

father has one of those, he spends more time with the birds than he does with his family. My mother is always complaining. Sometimes she wishes he'd just fly away and be done with it.'

'Well Molly, when you get older you'll find that's the time when you want to be alone. At least now and again, but not always.'

'I feel like that now. I love taking photographs but I'm afraid I haven't a clue. The Instamatic's my limit, but I'd like to do better. I'd even thought about ringing you but couldn't muster up the courage. Could I call and see you sometime? I'm thinking of buying a new camera, you know, a good 35 millimetre.'

Her lack of inhibition, energy and youthful enthusiasm dulled me into a state of grasping at time, of wanting to do the impossible and stop all the clocks in the world.

'Can I see your darkroom?'

'Well, there's not an awful lot to see. It's very dark in there. In fact it's probably the darkest place in Downpatrick,' I teased with prepared caution.

'Aye, it would have to be wouldn't it,' she laughed.

She was now teasing me and I admired her spirit.

'Don't worry, I'll advise you on the best make of camera to buy.'

I watched her pale, nimble fingers strike a match and then trawl the bursting flame across scorched tobacco in a deliberate left to right movement. The way she did it was beautiful and I remember thinking I'd never seen it done like that before. Her actions were almost African and panther-like, displaying an attitude of total unity between mind and body, something rarely found in Ireland where guilt was traditional and the confession box big in the world of crosses and chromosomes. Breaking the match with a quick flick of finger and thumb, she carelessly tossed it onto the tarmac where it bounced and rested.

'Are you married?' I asked.

'Married at nineteen, divorced at twenty six, just last year.'

'The old folk used to call it the seven year itch. Have you any children?'

For ten full seconds her moist eyes searched mine as if reading the obituary column in the morning paper, then slowly blinked once and looked away again.

'No children. I'd best be going, Mr Hanvey, I'll ring you. Oh! By the way, what takes you back to Downshire after all this time?

'I'm writing a book about my nursing days and I'm trying to get the feel of the place before I begin. You know what it's like.'

'That's a terrific idea. What's it going to be called?'

'The Mental.'

'And what else could you call it. Will I be in it?' she giggled with impish sincerity.

'I'd say you could possibly be in one of the chapters.'

'That's good. Then I'll buy it. Good luck with The Mental, Mr Hanvey. I'll ring you.'

As she walked away up through the same sad old trees

which held my best and worst memories, my eyes followed her with ageing despair until she stopped on the embankment and disappeared from sight.

Well what do you know, I mused. Imagine her calling me mister, I must be getting older by the minute.

Being fifty, they say is like standing on the threshold of loneliness. From then on you can be the centre of attraction in a room full of a hundred people and still feel the most forsaken person in the world. The only thing that generates respect in advancing years is the ageing process itself. By the time you hit the deathbed all you are left with is 'respect' or 'no respect'. In Downpatrick this was doled out by 'the respectable' most of whom were successful deviants of one kind or another and quite often the pillars of parochial society - guilt ridden donners of the hair shirt, their wives lost and lonely in a limbo of Matisse and Shawcross that new money acquired but had never quite learned to appreciate.

My mission to confront the ghosts of the past was only beginning, but I had one more stop to make before I said goodbye to the old place. In the Male One Corridor, the main artery that funnelled patients to the canteen, work and recreation, I sat down on one of the old green plastic covered chairs. It looked as if it hadn't budged in an age and I quietly waited for history to repeat itself.

Twenty minutes later nothing had happened. Not one single soul was to be seen as the light and shade created by the grey walls and tall narrow windows shimmered easily on the smartly buffed floor. Then suddenly, three old patients turned the far bottom corner with arms linked and moving at a menacing pace. The uneven dumpedy-dump, thumpedy-thump of slapping carpet slippers rose to a crescendo on that hollow floor. Two of them limped in irregular, awkward swaying movements, while the third, unaffected, tried hard to imitate their complicated steps, causing the hair to stand out on the back of my neck. Their faces, forever looking forward, turned and glared in my direction. Dead eyes stared from the depths of wrinkled wax as identical contorted smiles revealed yellowed teeth of ancient porcelain. High-pitched voices in demonic chant erupted on cue, as old limbs jiggled and jaggled and hobbled at speed.

'Cold day Nurse. Hell Nurse. You're a pishy fish nurse. Jibbidy, jibbidy jew, Nurse. Jibbidy, jibbidy jew. Jibbidy, jibbidy, jibbidy, jibbidy, jibbidy, jibbidy jew – ah ha, ha, ha, ha, ha, ha, ha'.

The unstoppable rumble of runaway feet grew louder and more intense only to die away seconds later on reaching the red, tiled semi-circle which hugged the outside of the Great Hall.

'What the hell was that?' I asked myself, before realising that I had been away from Downshire far too long.

The Bonzane triplets, detained at Her Majesty's pleasure during the early Sixties, for the murder of their mother, were three of the maddest, sickest psychos who'd ever walked the face of this terminally ill land.

Old age hadn't mellowed them.

I had been told that whenever or wherever in life I confronted naked anger, what I was really witnessing was the turmoil and hell of a troubled state of mind and I was well advised to let it be. I couldn't begin to imagine what was going on in the heads of the Bonzanes, but whatever it was it wasn't good.

Leaving mental nursing when I did was one of my better ideas. Books or lectures could never have given me such an insight on life. Staring madness in the face made it more easily recognisable in that beautiful world of 'sanity' outside the high perimeter walls.

In the early days, that long narrow corridor produced wave after wave of countless souls, from morning to night, with faces wearing every known expression under the sun. The smart, blue uniforms of the young female nurses and the brilliant white coats of their male counterparts peppered the throng as if captains in a cavalry charge. Now things were almost silent.

Downshire, one of the few remaining links to the Victorian era, had been successfully modified over the years and was now on its knees and pleading for mercy right before my eyes. It made me terribly sad. I had witnessed the cremation of my youth. Then suddenly, as I sat there, I saw it reappear again a hundred yards away at the end of this long, dark passageway.

The knee length white coat was clearly visible, even though it had been obsolete for years but my face in total shade was impossible to recognise. It simply could have been anyone.

This old place, which once generated my energy, was now sapping it from me and taking it back again.

Sadness, the emotion that sometimes keeps us alive, was coming at me like rain. It was like waiting for something that was never going to happen.